Statistics

Corequisite Workbook

for use with *Elementary Statistics 10e by*

Allan G. Bluman

Luis Beltran

Miami-Dade College, Kendall Campus

http://create.mheducation.com

ISBN-10: 1260516075   ISBN-13: 9781260516074

Table of Contents

This workbook is designed to provide corequisite remediation with an introductory statistics course. The topics included are mostly independent of one another and may be used in any order to match the structure of your course. Though the terminology and notation reflects that used in the *Elementary Statistics* and *Elementary Statistics: A Brief Version* textbooks, by Allan Bluman this workbook has been written in such a way that it could support a variety of textbooks. However, please note that the tables referenced in this workbook refer to those appearing in the Bluman *Elementary Statistics* titles.

Chapter 1 Number Sense, Variables and Types of Data

1.1 Real Number Sets

A **set** is a collection of objects called elements. These elements can be letters, numbers, days of the weeks, etc. The notation used is the braces notation { } with commas separating the elements within the set.

A **subset** is a set containing the same or fewer elements from another set. Thus, a subset is a set contained within another set.

In arithmetic, we define the following sets of numbers: Natural, Whole, Integer, Rational, Irrational and Real Number.

Natural (or counting) Numbers start at 1 and increase by one each time.
Natural Numbers = {1, 2, 3, 4, 5, 6, 7, 8, 9, 10,...}

Whole Numbers include all the Natural Numbers and 0.
Whole Numbers = {0, 1, 2, 3, 4, 5, 6, 7, 8, 9, 10,...}

Integers include all the Whole Numbers and their negatives.
Integers = {..., −10, −9, −8, −7, −6, −5, −4, −3, −2, −1, 0, 1, 2, 3, 4, 5, 6, 7, 8, 9, 10,...}

Rational Numbers are fractions in the form $\dfrac{a}{b}$ such that the numerator a and the denominator b are integers. The fraction $\dfrac{a}{b}$ may also be reduced to an integer. Therefore, the Rational Numbers include the integers.
Rational Numbers = $\left\{ \frac{a}{b}, \text{ where } a \text{ is an integer and } b \text{ is an integer} \neq 0 \right\}$

In decimal form, rational numbers are either terminating (such as 0.5, 0.129, 0.00001) or repeating decimals (such as $0.\overline{5}$, $0.\overline{3}$, $0.12\overline{9}$, $0.000131313\cdots$).

1

We observe that the set of Natural Numbers is a subset of the Whole Numbers. The set of Whole Numbers is a subset of the Integer Numbers. The set of Integer Numbers is a subset of the Rational Numbers. Therefore, all Natural, Whole and Integer Numbers are Rational Numbers, but not all Rational Numbers are Natural, Whole or Integer Numbers.

Irrational Numbers are numbers that cannot be expressed as rational numbers. In other words, in fraction form, the set of irrational numbers can be expressed as $\left\{\frac{a}{b}\right.$, where at least one of the values a or b is not an integer$\left.\right\}$
In decimal form, irrational numbers are non–terminating AND non–repeating decimals.

The sets of rational and irrational number form the Real Number system.
Although in algebra, we can extend this to the Complex Number system to include imaginary numbers, in statistics we work only with the Real Number system. As such, in this text, we will work only within the Real Number System.

Examples:
Classify the following as Rational and Irrational. If the number is rational, determine if it is also a Natural, Whole or Integer Number.

    a. −5
        Rational. Also: Integer.

    b. 27
        Rational. Also: Natural, Whole and Integer.

    c. $\frac{17}{41}$
        Rational only.

    d. $\frac{100}{25}$
        Rational. We can also reduce this to 4. This is also: Natural, Whole and Integer.

e. 0

Rational. Also: Whole and Integer.

f. $\frac{\sqrt{3}}{5}$

Irrational.

g. π

Irrational.

h. 0.158

This is a terminating decimal. Rational only.

i. $0.\overline{73}$

This is a repeating decimal. Rational only.

j. $\sqrt{16}$

We can reduce this to 4. Rational. Also: Natural, Whole and Integer.

k. $0.\overline{123456}$

This is a repeating decimal. Rational only.

l. 0.123456

This is a terminating decimal. Rational only.

m. 0.123456⋯⋯

This decimal does not repeat and does terminate. Irrational.

3

We can also use a number line to represent the real number system. We use the positive and negative infinity symbols ±∞ to represent that the number is infinite in both directions.

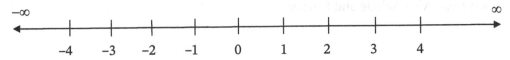

Your Turn to Practice

Classify the following as Rational and Irrational. If the number is rational, determine if it is also a Natural, Whole or Integer Number.

1. 35

2. –10

3. $\frac{36}{4}$

4. 7π

5. 0.542

6. $0.\overline{59}$

7. $\frac{11}{29}$

4

8. $\frac{\sqrt{2}}{2}$

9. $0.474474447\cdots$

10. 0

11. $\sqrt{49}$

1.2 Define the Symbols $<,>,\leq,\geq$

When comparing numbers, we use either equality or inequality symbols. When the numbers are the same or equal in value when use the "equals" symbol $=$. For values that are strictly not equal we can use the "not equal to" symbol $\neq$. To further illustrate which value is larger or smaller, we use the inequality symbols of "less than" $<$ or "greater than."

Examples:
Compare these numbers using the symbols $<$, $>$ or $=$.

a. $5 \ \square \ 10$

   5 is less than 10. $\qquad$ $5 \ \boxed{<} \ 10$

b. $7 \ \square \ 3$

   7 is greater than 3. $\qquad$ $7 \ \boxed{>} \ 3$

c. $\sqrt{81}$ ☐ 9

The values are equal. $\sqrt{81}$ $\boxed{=}$ 9

d. −10 ☐ −12

−10 is greater than −12. −10 $\boxed{>}$ −12

e. 0.3 ☐ $0.\overline{3}$

0.3 is less than 0.3333⋯. 0.3 $\boxed{<}$ 0.3333⋯

0.3 $\boxed{<}$ $0.\overline{3}$

f. $\dfrac{5}{9}$ ☐ $\dfrac{10}{13}$

$\dfrac{5}{9}$ is less than $\dfrac{10}{13}$. $\dfrac{5}{9}$ $\boxed{<}$ $\dfrac{10}{13}$

g. $\dfrac{1}{2}$ ☐ 0.5%

$\dfrac{1}{2}$ is greater than 0.5% $\dfrac{1}{2}$ $\boxed{>}$ 0.5%

h. 99.99% ☐ 1

6

99.99% is less than 100% , which is equivalent to 1   99.99% $\boxed{<}$ 100%

99.99% $\boxed{<}$ 1

Your Turn to Practice

Compare these numbers using the symbols $<$, $>$ or $=$.

1. 11 $\boxed{\phantom{<}}$ 19

2. -20 $\boxed{\phantom{<}}$ -10

3. 6 $\boxed{\phantom{<}}$ $\sqrt{36}$

4. $0.\overline{12}$ $\boxed{\phantom{<}}$ 0.12

5. $\dfrac{11}{12}$ $\boxed{\phantom{<}}$ $\dfrac{8}{9}$

6. $\dfrac{1}{2}$% $\boxed{\phantom{<}}$ 0.5

7. 100% $\boxed{\phantom{<}}$ 99.999999%

We can also use the "less than OR equal to" symbol $\leq$ and the "greater than OR equal to" symbol $\geq$. In either one of these two cases the inequality is satisfied if the numbers are equal OR if the inequality $<$ or $>$ statement is true.

If $a \leq b$, then either $a < b$ OR $a = b$.

If $a \geq b$, then either $a > b$ OR $a = b$.

7

Examples:

Determine if the given statement is True or False.

    a. $6 \leq 10$

       True since 6 is less than 10.

    b. $7 \geq 7$

       True since 7 is equal to 7.

    c. $-20 \geq -15$

       False, since neither $-20 > -15$ nor $-20 = -15$ is true.

    d. $\dfrac{1}{2} \geq \dfrac{3}{7}$

       True since $\dfrac{1}{2} > \dfrac{3}{7}$.

Your Turn to Practice

Determine if the given statement is True or False.

1. $100\% \geq 1$

2. $19 \geq 25$

3. $-9 \leq -2$

4. $\dfrac{1}{2} \leq 0.5\%$

5. $\dfrac{4}{9} \leq 0.\overline{4}$

8

1.3 Order of Operations

In mathematics, when performing various operations such as addition, subtraction, multiplication, division, exponents and the inclusion of parentheses, we follow an order that indicates which operation must be done first. This is known as the order of operations.

    1st Simplify inside the Parentheses.

    2nd Simplify Exponents.

    3rd Multiply and Divide. If Multiplication and Division are together, then simplify whichever comes first from left to right.

    4th Add and Subtract.

A common tool to help students is the pneumonic **P**lease **E**xcuse **M**y **D**ear **A**unt **S**ally also known as PEMDAS.

Examples:

Simplify.

    a. $-9 + 8^2 - 2(-3)$

$$\begin{aligned}
&-9 + 8^2 - 2(-3) && \textit{Simplify first the exponent} \\
={}& -9 + 64 - 2(-3) && \textit{Multiply} \\
={}& -9 + 64 + 6 && \textit{Add and Subtract} \\
={}& 61
\end{aligned}$$

    b. $-3(5 - 3^2) - 32 \div 8(-2)$

$$\begin{aligned}
&-3(5 - 3^2) - 32 \div 8(-2) && \textit{Simplify first the exponent (only the 3 is squared)} \\
={}& -3(5 - 9) - 32 \div 8(-2) && \textit{Simplify inside the parenthesis} \\
={}& -3(-4) - 32 \div 8(-2) && \textit{Multiply/Divide. Left to right: divide first} \\
={}& -3(-4) - 4(-2) && \textit{Multiply} \\
={}& 12 + 8 && \textit{Add} \\
={}& 20
\end{aligned}$$

c. $\sqrt{\dfrac{5(50)-12^2}{5(5-1)}}$

$\sqrt{\dfrac{5(50)-12^2}{5(5-1)}}$ *Simplify inside the parenthesis*

$= \sqrt{\dfrac{5(50)-12^2}{5(4)}}$ *Simplify the exponent (only the 12 is squared)*

$= \sqrt{\dfrac{5(50)-144}{5(4)}}$ *Multiply*

$= \sqrt{\dfrac{250-144}{20}}$ *Simplify inside the numerator*

$= \sqrt{\dfrac{106}{20}}$ *Divide*

$= \sqrt{5.3} \approx 2.30$

Your Turn to Practice

Simplify.

1. $(8-3)(9-7)$

2. $7^2 + 4^2$

3. $-10 + 7^2 - 5(-4)$

10

4. $-4(23-5^2)-70\div10(-7)$

5. $\dfrac{-9^2-3^3}{(10-7)(11-15)}$

6. $\sqrt{\dfrac{6(20)-3^2}{6(6-1)}}$

7. $\dfrac{\dfrac{11}{15}}{\dfrac{14}{15}}$

1.4 Compute Boundaries of a Number

The boundaries of a number are the intervals, also known as classes or class intervals, in which a value is contained. The original number is the midpoint of the class boundaries. Each class cutoff value contains the digit five with one more decimal place than the original number. In other words, if the original number is a whole number then the boundaries

11

contain one decimal place (to the nearest tenths place). If the original number is a decimal with one place value then the boundaries contain two decimal places (to the nearest hundredths place), and so on.

Examples:

Find the boundaries for the following numbers.

a. 33

Since 33 is a whole number, the class boundaries will contain one decimal place (to the nearest tenths place). Add 0.5 to 33 and get 33.5 for the upper boundary. Subtract 0.5 from 33 and get 32.5 for the lower boundary. So the boundaries for 33 are 32.5 – 33.5.

b. 54.5

Since 54.5 contains one decimal place, the class boundaries will contain two decimal places (to the nearest hundredths place). Add 0.05 to 54.5 and get 54.55 for the upper boundary. Subtract 0.05 from 54.5 and get 54.45 for the lower boundary. So the boundaries for 54.5 are 54.45 – 54.55.

c. 79.643

Since 79.643 contains three decimal places, the class boundaries will contain four decimal places (to the nearest ten-thousandths place). Add 0.0005 to 79.643 and get 79.6435 for the upper boundary. Subtract 0.0005 from 79.643 and get 79.6425 for the lower boundary. So the boundaries for 79.643 are 79.6425 – 79.6435.

d. 0.0015

Since 0.0015 contains four decimal places, the class boundaries will contain five decimal places (to the nearest hundred-thousandths place). Add 0.00005 to 0.0015 and get 0.00155 for the upper boundary. Subtract 0.00005 from 0.0015 and get

0.00145 for the lower boundary. So the boundaries for 0.0015 are 0.00145 – 0.00155.

Your Turn to Practice

Find the boundaries for the following numbers.

1. 35.6

2. 0.0002349

3. 2.7481

4. 57

5. 1.98

6. 13.25

1.5 Define Nominal, Ordinal, Interval and Ratio Levels of Measurement

In statistics, when collecting data, we use measurement scales to classify the data. The **nominal level** of measurement is when data is classified by name. The **ordinal level** of

13

measurement is when data is classified in some sort of order. The **interval level** of measurement is when data can be classified by numerical differences with no absolute zero defined. The **ratio level** of measurement is similar to the interval level of measurement but an absolute zero is defined.

Examples:
Identify the level of measurement in each case.

   a. Temperature reading in a classroom in degrees Fahrenheit
   Interval, since there are differences between temperature readings. A reading of $90°F$ is $10°F$ warmer than a reading of $80°F$. It is not ratio since $0°F$ is not an absolute zero.

   b. Political Party Affiliation of registered Floridians
   Nominal, since the classifications are names. For example, registered Floridians may be identified as Democrat, Republican, Independent, Green, etc.

   c. Weights of Olympic athletes
   Ratio, since there are differences between weights and there is an absolute zero. In a weight scale, the first value we see is 0 (whether is in pounds, ounces, kilograms, liters, etc.).

   d. Ranking Olympic winners by trophy (Gold, Silver, Bronze)
   Ordinal since the classifications have meaning based on their ranking. For example, Gold is the top prize. Silver is in second place, while bronze is in third place.

   e. Students identified by their major (Psychology, Medicine, Mathematics, etc.)
   Nominal since the classifications are names. For example, these students may be identified as majoring in Psychology, Medicine, Mathematics, etc.

Your Turn to Practice

Identify the level of measurement in each case.

1. Heights of basketball players

2. Lotto prizes identified as the number one prize followed by the second, third and forth

3. High School students enrolled in a foreign language course are identified by their course: French, German, Italian and Spanish

4. Temperature in Alaska in degrees Celsius throughout the month of January

5. Super Bowl fans identified as fans of Team A, Team B or undecided

Chapter 2 Frequency Distributions

2.1 Decimal Place Value and Rounding Rules

Before constructing frequency tables, we begin this chapter with a review of decimal place values and rules for rounding numbers. These rounding rules will be applied when computing relative frequencies, cumulative frequencies, class midpoints and class boundaries that must be rounded off.

If a number is a whole number, the last digit in the whole number is the ones place. The next place to the left of the ones place is the tens place, then the next place to the left is the hundreds, then the thousands, ten-thousands, hundred-thousands, millions, ten-millions, hundred-millions, billions, etc.

If the number contains a decimal, the first place value after the decimal point is the tenths place. The next place to the right of tenths place is the hundredths, followed by the thousandths, ten-thousandths, hundred-thousandths, millionths, ten-millionths, hundred-millionths, billionths, etc.

Examples:

Identify the place value for every digit for the given number.

   a. 156

       6 is in the ones places
       5 is in the tens place
       1 is in the hundreds place

b. 27,396,804

4 is in the ones places
0 is in the tens place
8 is in the hundreds place
6 is in the thousands place
9 is in the ten-thousands place
3 is in the hundred-thousands place
7 is in the millions place
2 is in the ten-millions place

c. 89.57324

8 is in the tens place
9 is in the ones places
5 is in the tenths place
7 is in the hundredths place
3 is in the thousandths place
2 is in the ten-thousandths place
4 is in the hundred-thousandths place

Your Turn to Practice

Identify the place value for every digit for the given number.

1. 20,864

2. 579.48631

We will apply the rounding rules numbers that are typically used in Math which is to use the cutoff of the digit 5.

When rounding a number:

- If the digit following the rounded digit is greater than or equal to 5, then the rounded digit is increased by 1.
- If the digit following the rounded digit is less than 5, then the rounded digit remains the same.

In some instances, rounding to a specific place value may not be the most effective rounding rule. For example, when there are numbers smaller than 0.001 such as 0.0004 or 0.000099, if we round to the nearest tenths or hundredths we obtain 0.0 or 0.00. Although the rounding is correct, we will have numbers that may not accurately represent the value of the original number. In these cases, we use significant digits (or significant figures) for rounding. Significant digits are the digits remaining in the rounded answer and are used to provide the most accurate approximation. These significant digits are counted from left to right where the first digit from the left is always a non-zero digit while the last digit on the right may or may not be a zero. For numbers in decimal form that are rounded to a place value after the decimal point (tenths, hundredths, thousandths, etc.), the significant digits are counted from the first non-zero digit appearing to the right of the decimal point.

Examples:

Round the given number to the specified decimal place.

a. Round 648.10591 to the nearest whole number

Since we are asked to round to the nearest whole number, we need to look at the tenths place. The value 1 is in the tenths place. Since 1 is less than 5, we round down to the nearest whole number, so the 8 remains the same.

The rounded answer is 648.

Note: had the value in the tenths place been 5, 6, 7, 8, or 9, we would round up to the nearest whole number, so the 8 would change to a 9 and the rounded answer would be 649.

b. Round 648.10593 to the nearest tenths place

Since we are asked to round to the nearest tenths place, we need to look at the hundredths place. The value 0 is in the hundredths place. Since 0 is less than 5, we round down to the nearest tenths place, so the 1 stays the same.

The rounded answer is 648.1.

c. Round 8,265.7394 to the nearest hundreds place

Since we are asked to round to the nearest hundreds place, we need to look at the tens place. The value 6 is in the tenths place. Since 6 is greater than 5, we round 2 up to 3 and we place zeros after the 3 up to the ones place.

The rounded answer is 8,300.

d. Round 8,265.7394 to the nearest hundredths place

Since we are asked to round to the nearest hundredths place, we need to look at the thousandths place. The value 9 is in the thousandths place. Since 9 is greater than 5, we round 3 up to 4.

The rounded answer is 8,275.74.

e. Round 0.027986 to the nearest tenths place

Since we are asked to round to the nearest tenths place, we need to look at the hundredths place. The value 2 is in the hundredths place. Since 2 is less than 5, the 0 in the tenths place stays the same.

Rounded answer is 0.0 *Note: you must leave your answer as 0.0 and not just 0 in order to represent the rounded place value.*

f. Round 0.027986 to the nearest hundredths place

Since we are asked to round to the nearest hundredths place, we need to look at the thousandths place. The value 7 is in the thousandths place. Since 7 is greater than 5, the 2 in the hundredths place is rounded up to 3.

The rounded answer is 0.03.

g. Round 0.027986 to the nearest ten-thousandths place

Since we are asked to round to the nearest ten-thousandths place, we need to look at the hundred-thousandths place. The value 8 is in the hundred-thousandths place. Since 8 is greater than 5, the 9 in the ten-thousandths place is rounded up to 10. Since 10 is greater than 9, we move over to the thousandths place and increase the 7 to 8.

The rounded answer is 0.0280. *Note: you must leave your answer as 0.0280 and not 0.028 to illustrate the rounded place value.*

Round the given number to the specified number of significant digits.

h. Round 0.0000170633 to two significant digits

The first significant digit is 1.

The first *two* significant digits are 1 and 7. The digit 7 is followed by 0 which is less than 5. So, 7 stays the same.

The rounded answer to two significant digits is 0.000017.

i. Round 0.0000170633 to three significant digits

The first significant digit is 1.

The first *three* significant digits are 1, 7, and 0. The digit 0 is followed by 6 which is greater than 5. So, the 0 is rounded up to 1.

The rounded answer to three significant digits is 0.0000171.

j. Round 0.0000170633 to four significant digits

The first *four* significant digits are 1, 7, 0, and 6. The digit 6 is followed by 3 which is less than 5. So, the 6 stays the same.

The rounded answer to four significant digits is 0.00001706.

Your Turn to Practice

1. Round 29.4996 to the nearest tenths place

2. Round 29.4996 to the nearest thousandths place

3. Round 32,594.0507 to the nearest thousands place

4. Round 32,594.0507 to the nearest hundredths place

5. Round 97.8493 to the nearest whole number

6. Round 97.8493 to the nearest whole number

7. Round 0.00086513 to the nearest hundredths place

8. Round 0.00086513 to two significant digits

9. Round 0.00086513 to three significant digits

10. Round 0.00000021475 to three significant digits

2.2 Compute a Percentage

In this section, we learn how to compute a percentage. A percentage is a quantity out of 100 represented by the % symbol. So 60% means 60 out of 100. While 0.60% means 0.60 out of 100. These two numbers are very different, so it important to place the decimal point correctly.

To convert from a fraction to a decimal and then to a percent, we just divide the numerator by the denominator and then convert the decimal answer to a percent.

These are two simple shortcuts for quickly converting a decimal to a percent and a percent to a decimal.

Decimal to Percent conversion: Move the decimal two places to the right and place the % symbol at the end.

Percent to Decimal conversion: Remove the % symbol and move the decimal two places to the left.

Examples:

Convert the following to percentages.

    a. 0.96

       Move the decimal two places to the right after the 6 and place the % symbol at the end.

       We obtain 96%.

    b. 0.05

       Move the decimal two places to the right after the 5 and place the % symbol at the end.

       We obtain 5%.

c. 1.2

Move the decimal two places to the right. We need to add a zero. The decimal is after the zero and place the % symbol at the end.

We obtain 120%.

d. $\dfrac{2}{25}$

Convert the fraction to the decimal 0.08. Move the decimal two places to the right after the 8 and place the % symbol at the end.

We obtain 4%.

e. $\dfrac{17}{100}$

Since 17 is already out of 100, we can quickly obtain 17% without having to write the decimal.

f. $\dfrac{39}{47}$

Convert the fraction to the decimal 0.829787234. We need to round the decimal. We can round it to two, three, or four significant digits.

Two significant digits rounds to 0.83. Move the decimal two places to the right after the 3 and place the % symbol at the end.

We obtain 83%.

Three significant digits rounds to 0.830. Move the decimal two places to the right after the 3 and place the % symbol at the end.

We obtain 83.0%.

Four significant digits rounds to 0.8298. Move the decimal two places to the right after the 2 and place the % symbol at the end.

We obtain 82.98%.

g. $\dfrac{41}{103}$

Convert the fraction to the decimal 0.398058252. We need to round the decimal. We can round it to two, three, or four significant digits.

Two significant digits rounds to 0.40. Move the decimal two places to the right after the 0 and place the % symbol at the end.

We obtain 40%.

Three significant digits rounds to 0.398. Move the decimal two places to the right after the 9 and place the % symbol at the end.

We obtain 39.8%.

Four significant digits rounds to 0.3981. Move the decimal two places to the right after the 9 and place the % symbol at the end.

We obtain 39.81%.

26

Convert the percentages to decimals.

h. 23%

Remove the % symbol and move the decimal two places to the left in front of the 2.

We obtain 0.23.

i. 4.99%

Remove the % symbol and move the decimal two places to the left. We need to place a 0 in front of the 4. The decimal is in front of the 0.

We obtain 0.0499.

j. 0.00000712%

Remove the % symbol and move the decimal two places to the left. We need to insert two additional zeros between the decimal point and the digit 7. So, now we have seven zeros between the decimal point and the digit 7.

We obtain 0.0000000712.

k. 150%

Remove the % symbol and move the decimal two places to the left in front of the 5.

We obtain 1.5.

1. 0.2%

Remove the % symbol and move the decimal two places to the left. We need to insert two zeros between the decimal point and the digit 2.

We obtain 0.002.

Your Turn to Practice

Convert the following to percentages.

1. 5.3

2. 0.029

3. $\frac{22}{50}$

4. $\frac{3}{4}$

5. 0.47

6. $\frac{56}{97}$

7. 0.000094

8. $\frac{2}{3}$

Convert the percentages to decimals.

9. 1.987%

10. 64%

11. 100%

12. 0.5%

13. 0.00354%

14. 260%

15. 99

2.3 Compute Cumulative Frequencies

In this section, we can find the cumulative frequency of each category (or class interval) by computing the total of the frequencies up to and including the frequency of the category (or class interval).

Example:

In a class of 40 students the distribution of grades for the semester was the following.

Grade	Number of Students (Frequency)
A	4
B	14
C	15
D	5
F	2

Using the table, compute each cumulative frequency and then organize them in a new table.

For the A's, the cumulative frequency is 4 since only the 4 from that group have been totaled.

For the B's, 14 more have occurred so the cumulative frequency is 4 +14 = 18.

For the C's, 15 more have occurred so the cumulative frequency is 18 +15 = 33.

For the D's, 5 more have occurred so the cumulative frequency is 33 +5 = 38.

For the F's, 2 more have occurred so the cumulative frequency is 38 +2 = 40.

Observe, that the last cumulative frequency 40 is equal to the total in the group. This must always occur since the last cumulative frequency has accumulated all frequency values.

We can then organize the table for the distribution of grades using the cumulative frequencies in place of the original frequencies.

Grade	Number of Students (Cumulative Frequency)
A	4
B	18
C	33
D	38
F	40

Your Turn to Practice

Compute the cumulative frequency for each interval in the table. Then organize the table using the cumulative frequencies in place of the original frequencies.

The number of minutes spent on one phone call	Number of people (Frequency)
-0.5 – 5.5	8
5.5 – 10.5	40
10.5 – 15.5	16
15.5 – 20.5	6
20.5 – 25.5	4
25.5 – 30.5	3
30.5 – 35.5	2
Above 35.5	1

The number of minutes spent on one phone call	Cumulative Number of people (Cumulative Frequency)
-0.5 – 5.5	
5.5 – 10.5	
10.5 – 15.5	
15.5 – 20.5	
20.5 – 25.5	
25.5 – 30.5	
30.5 – 35.5	
Above 35.5	

2.4 Change Relative Frequency and Cumulative Relative Frequency to a Percentage

In this section, we can compute relative frequencies and cumulative relative frequencies from a given frequency table. We can then express these relative frequencies as proportions in decimal form. Although it is not required, we can also convert the relative frequencies to percentages to illustrate the percentage of values that occur in each class.

The relative frequency is the frequency, f, of the given class out of the total in the group which equals the sum of the frequencies, n.

$$\text{Relative Frequency} = \frac{f}{n}$$

$$\text{Percentage of Values} = \frac{f}{n} \cdot 100 \text{ converts it to a \%}$$

Additionally, we can compute the cumulative relative frequency by the finding the total of the relative frequencies up to and including the relative frequency of the category (or class interval).

Example:

From the example in Section 2.3, the distribution of grades for 40 students was given in the frequency table below.

Grade	Number of Students (Frequency)
A	4
B	14
C	15
D	5
F	2

Since the total number of students is 40, we compute each relative frequency by dividing each frequency, f, by $n = 40$. Additionally, we can find the percentage of values for each.

Therefore, each relative frequency and % of values is:

$\dfrac{4}{40} = 0.10$ or 10% for the A's

$\dfrac{14}{40} = 0.35$ or 35% for the B's

$\dfrac{15}{40} = 0.375$ or 37.5% for the C's

$$\frac{5}{40} = 0.125 \text{ or } 12.5\% \text{ for the D's}$$

$$\frac{2}{40} = 0.05 \text{ or } 5\% \text{ for the F's}$$

We can then organize the table for the distribution of grades using the relative frequencies as proportions in decimal form in place of the original frequencies.

Grade	Relative Frequency
A	0.10
B	0.35
C	0.375
D	0.125
F	0.05

We can also convert the relative frequencies to percentages.

Grade	% of Students
A	10%
B	35%
C	37.5%
D	12.5%
F	5%

To find the cumulative relative frequency of each letter grade, we begin with the first category A. 0.10 is the percentage that has accumulated thus far. Then for the B category, we add $0.10 + 0.35 = 0.45$. Then for the C category, we add $0.45 + 0.375 = 0.825$. Then for the D category, we add $0.825 + 0.125 = 0.95$. For the last category F, we add $0.95 + 0.05 = 1$. It will always be the case that the last category totals up to 1.00. This is logical since the last category includes all previous categories.

We can then organize the table for the distribution of grades using the cumulative relative frequencies in decimal form in place of the relative frequencies.

Grade	Cumulative Relative Frequency
A	0.10
B	0.45
C	0.825
D	0.95
F	1.00

We can also convert the cumulative relative frequencies to percentages.

Grade	Cumulative % of Students
A	10%
B	45%
C	82.5%
D	95%
F	100%

Your Turn to Practice

Compute the relative frequency for each interval in the table. Then organize the table using the relative frequencies in decimal form in place of the original frequencies. Construct another table illustrating the % of values in each class.

Using the same information, compute the cumulative relative frequencies from the table of relative frequencies in decimal form. Then organize the table using the cumulative relative frequencies in decimal form in place of the relative frequencies. Construct another table illustrating the cumulative % of values in each class.

The number of minutes spent on one phone call	Number of people (Frequency)
-0.5 – 5.5	8
5.5 – 10.5	40
10.5 – 15.5	16
15.5 – 20.5	6
20.5 – 25.5	4
25.5 – 30.5	3
30.5 – 35.5	2
Above 35.5	1

The number of minutes spent on one phone call	Relative Frequency
-0.5 – 5.5	
5.5 – 10.5	
10.5 – 15.5	
15.5 – 20.5	
20.5 – 25.5	
25.5 – 30.5	
30.5 – 35.5	
Above 35.5	

The number of minutes spent on one phone call	% of people
-0.5 – 5.5	
5.5 – 10.5	
10.5 – 15.5	
15.5 – 20.5	
20.5 – 25.5	
25.5 – 30.5	
30.5 – 35.5	
Above 35.5	

The number of minutes spent on one phone call	Cumulative Relative Frequency
-0.5 – 5.5	
5.5 – 10.5	
10.5 – 15.5	
15.5 – 20.5	
20.5 – 25.5	
25.5 – 30.5	
30.5 – 35.5	
Above 35.5	

The number of minutes spent on one phone call	Cumulative % of people
-0.5 – 5.5	
5.5 – 10.5	
10.5 – 15.5	
15.5 – 20.5	
20.5 – 25.5	
25.5 – 30.5	
30.5 – 35.5	
Above 35.5	

2.5 Compute the Midpoint

Midpoint of a class interval

When working with a grouped frequency table, it is useful and sometimes necessary to identify the midpoint of each class interval. To compute the midpoint each class interval, you need find the sum of the higher and lower limits of the interval and divide by two. An easy was to remember is to say that the midpoint is the average value of the lower and higher class limits.

$$\text{Midpoint} = \frac{\text{Lower Limit} + \text{Higher Limit}}{2}$$

To find each class midpoint, we can apply the formula to each interval. A shortcut would to just find the midpoint of the first class and then add the class width. We can find the class width by finding the difference between two consecutive lower limits or two consecutive lower limits. Two consecutive pairs of midpoints will also differ by the same class width.

Example:

A survey of 100 Statistics students was conducted to determine the average time in minutes it takes to complete their daily assignments. The results are given below in the following grouped frequency table in which the minutes are grouped into class intervals. Find the class midpoints.

The number of minutes spent on the assignments	Number of Students (Frequency)
10 – 19	10
20 – 29	39
30 – 39	44
40 – 49	4
50 – 59	2
60 – 69	1

The midpoints are: $\dfrac{10+19}{2}=14.5$ $\dfrac{20+29}{2}=24.5$ $\dfrac{30+39}{2}=34.5$

$\dfrac{40+49}{2}=44.5$ $\dfrac{50+59}{2}=54.5$ $\dfrac{60+69}{2}=64.5$

ALTERNATE APPROACH: From the original class limits, we can identify the class width by finding the difference between two consecutive lower limits or two consecutive lower limits. The class width is 10. After finding the first midpoint, we can find the rest by adding 10 each time until we have found all the midpoints.

The first midpoint is $\dfrac{10+19}{2}=14.5$. Then add 10 to get 24.5. Then add 10 more to get 34.5.

Then add 10 again to get 44.5. Then add 10 again to get 54.5. Then add 10 one last time to get 64.5.

We can then organize the table using the class midpoints in place of the original class limits.

The number of minutes spent on the assignments (Midpoints)	Number of Students (Frequency)
14.5	10
24.5	39
34.5	44
44.5	4
54.5	2
64.5	1

Midpoint of an upper limit and next consecutive lower limit to compute class boundaries.

Another kind of midpoint that we can find is the midpoint between any upper limit and the next consecutive lower limit. This value is called a class boundary and is used to replace the upper limit and next consecutive lower limit. The class boundaries can be used to graphically represent the data using a bar known as a histogram.

Example:

Using the table from the previous example, find the class boundaries.

The number of minutes spent on the assignments	Number of Students (Frequency)
10 – 19	10
20 – 29	39
30 – 39	44
40 – 49	4
50 – 59	2
60 – 69	1

We compute the midpoint of the first upper class limit 19 and the next consecutive lower limit 20. $\dfrac{19+20}{2}=19.5$ We replace 19 and 20 with the boundary 19.5. We can add 10 to compute the remaining upper and lower limits.

$19.5 + 10 = 29.5$ $29.5 + 10 = 39.5$ $39.5 + 10 = 49.5$

$49.5 + 10 = 59.5$ $59.5 + 10 = 69.5$

We can then organize the table for using the class boundaries in place of the original class limits. The first boundary can be computed by subtracting 10 from 19.5 which gives 9.5.

The number of minutes spent on the assignments (class boundaries)	Number of Students (Frequency)
9.5 – 19.5	10
19.5 – 29.5	39
29.5 – 39.5	44
39.5 – 49.5	4
49.5 – 59.5	2
59.5 – 69.5	1

Your Turn to Practice

The given grouped frequency table represents the number of minutes 60 shoppers spent shopping on-line on a weekday. Find the class midpoints and class boundaries.

The number of minutes shopping on-line	Number of people (Frequency)
0.0 – 10.4	10
10.5 – 20.9	19
21.0 – 31.4	11
31.5 – 41.9	8
42.0 – 52.4	9
52.5 – 62.9	1
63.0 – 73.4	2

The number of minutes shopping on-line (Class Midpoints)	Number of people (Frequency)
	10
	19
	11
	8
	9
	1
	2

The number of minutes shopping on-line (Class Boundaries)	Number of people (Frequency)
	10
	19
	11
	8
	9
	1
	2

2.6 Read Information from Tables, Charts, and Graphs

In statistics, we use different types of tables, charts, and graphs to interpret data.

Examples:

Below are some examples of EXCEL charts. Interpret the information.

Answers may vary.

a. Interpret the data from the given frequency table.

The number of minutes spent on the assignments	Number of Students (Frequency)
10 – 19	10
20 – 29	39
30 – 39	44
40 – 49	4
50 – 59	2
60 – 69	1

<u>One conclusion:</u> Most students spent somewhere between 30 to 39 minutes completing their assignments. Using the class midpoint, we could also say that the most time spent was approximately 34.5 minutes.

<u>Another conclusion:</u> Few students spend more than 40 minutes to complete their assignments.

b. Interpret the data from the given pie chart.

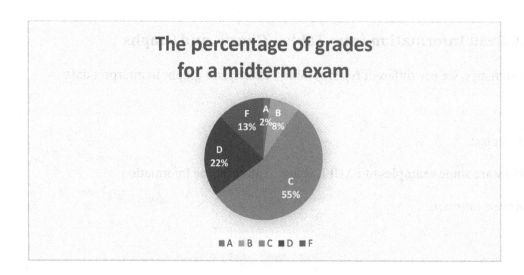

One conclusion: Only a small percentage of students did very well on the midterm exam.

Another conclusion: 65% of the class passed the midterm where passing means a C or higher.

Your Turn to Practice

1. Interpret the data from the given pie chart.

2. Interpret the data from the given frequency table.

The number of minutes shopping online	Number of people (Frequency)
0.0 – 10.4	10
10.5 – 20.9	19
21.0 – 31.4	11
31.5 – 41.9	8
42.0 – 52.4	9
52.5 – 62.9	1
63.0 – 73.4	2

3. Interpret the data from the given bar graphs. The second bar graph is called a Pareto Chart. What is the obvious characteristic of the Pareto Chart?

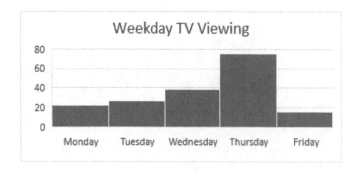

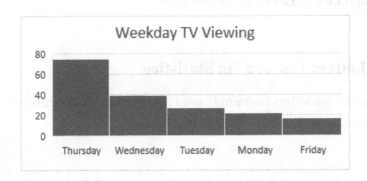

The Greek letter sigma, Σ, appears quite familiar to the uninitiated. The blocked letters shown are sigma's meant to represent the population standard deviation. Sometimes, for instance, on the standard version of SPSS, overseas sigma appears in the box of the values of the population left to the lower letter's lower in tables if sample... the mode... called a coefficient mean the assessment until of hot to... but once we live to represent the measure average of the population.

4. Interpret the data from the given Pareto Chart.

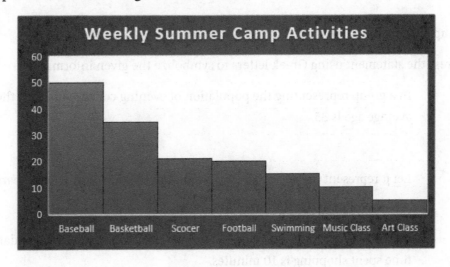

Chapter 3 Descriptive Statistics Skills

3.1 Define the Greek Letters $\sum$, μ, σ, σ^2 in Statistics

In this section, we review the Greek letters commonly used in statistics. We typically use Greek letters to represent the values obtained from a population.

The Greek letter capital sigma, $\sum$, appears quite a bit in mathematics and statistics. It represents the sum or summation symbol. The Greek letter lowercase sigma, σ, is used in statistics to represent the population standard deviation. In statistics, the variance equals the standard deviation squared. Therefore, lowercase sigma squared, σ^2, is used statistics to represent the variance of the population. The Greek letter μ is used in many applications in mathematics and the sciences to represent the measurement unit micro (e.g., μm represents micrometers). However, in statistics we use μ to represent the mean (or average) of the population.

Examples:

Express the statement using Greek letters to symbolize the given information.

    a.   In a group representing the population of evening college students, the overall average age is 35.

        Let μ represent the average of the population, then we say $\mu = 35$ years.

    b.   In a group representing the population of online shoppers, the standard deviation time spent shopping is 10 minutes.

        Let σ represent the standard deviation of the population, then we say $\sigma = 10$ minutes.

c. In a factory of alkaline batteries, the population variance for the lifespan of a battery after its first use is assumed to be 25 hours squared.

Let σ represent the standard deviation of the population and the variance equals the standard deviation squared, then we say $\sigma^2 = 25$ hours squared.

Your Turn to Practice

Given the following statement in Greek letters, rewrite the statement in words.

1. Height (in inches) of young adult males. $\sigma^2 = 36$

2. Travel time (in minutes) to work in the morning. $\sigma = 16$

3. Lifespan (in years) of factory paint for automobiles. $\mu = 10$

3.2 Using Subscript Notation

In mathematics, we have the option of using different letters or the same letter with subscripts as variables to represent different values. If we have 5 values, we could use the letters a, b, c, d and e or we could use the same letter a but with a subscript to represent each of the values. With subscripts on a, we can represent the first as a_1, the second as a_2, the third as a_3, the forth as a_4 and the fifth as a_5. In general, we define a_n is the nth term in the data set. [*Note: Since the original values in the data set do not have to be in increasing order, the subscripts simply represent the position of each value.*]

Examples:

    a. Using the variable X, denote each value using a subscript. 13, 20, 56, 57, 98, 100

$$X_1 = 13 \quad X_2 = 20 \quad X_3 = 56 \quad X_4 = 57 \quad X_5 = 98 \quad X_6 = 100$$

    b. Using the variable X, denote each value using a subscript. 63, 81, 2, 19, 50

We observe that the numbers are not in order so the first value, 63, is represented as $X_1 = 63$. The second value is represented as $X_2 = 81$, and so on.

Thus, each value is then represented as:

$$X_1 = 63 \quad X_2 = 81 \quad X_3 = 2 \quad X_4 = 19 \quad X_5 = 50$$

<u>Your Turn to Practice</u>

1. Identify the value of each variable for the set of numbers.

   1.3 5.2 13.0 26.5 44.7 50.7 52.4 61.2 61.5 61.8 73.2 77.5

   a. X_1

   b. X_2

   c. X_5

   d. X_8

   e. X_{10}

   f. X_{12}

2. Identify the value of each variable for the set of numbers.

   100.26 94.56 79.26 58.97 99.22 81.05 77.10

   a. X_1

   b. X_2

   c. X_3

   d. X_4

e. X_5

f. X_6

g. X_7

3.3 Compute an Average

In statistics, the mean is the average value of a group of numbers. Let's review the computation of an average. In simple terms, we add up all the numbers and divide by the total number of values to compute their average.

Example:

A student takes 4 exams and wants to find their average grade. All tests have the same number of total possible points in this class. Test grades are: 84, 86, 65, 77.

We add up the 4 test scores: $84 + 86 + 65 + 77 = 312$

Divide the total by 4 since there are 4 test scores. $\frac{312}{4} = 78$.

So, the student's average is a 78.

We can generate a formula for computing the average (or mean) of a group of values. Each value is a different X represented as $X_1, X_2, X_3, X_4, \dots$ Now, using the $\sum$ notation we defined in Section 3.1, the sum of all X values is $\sum X = X_1 + X_2 + X_3, + X_4, \dots$ and letting n represent the total number of numbers (or scores) in a sample group and each number is X, we can define the average as the $\sum X$ divided by n which can be expressed as the fraction $\frac{\sum X}{n}$. To further differentiate between the average of the population and the average of a sample, we use capital N for the number of values in the population group and lower case n for the number of values in the sample. We denote the average (or mean) of the population using

52

the Greek letter, μ, and the average (or mean) of the sample using the notation, $\overline{X}$ read as "X-bar." We then obtain the following formulas:

$$\overline{X} = \frac{\sum X}{n} \qquad\qquad \mu = \frac{\sum X}{n}$$

In our previous example, with the values 84, 86, 65, 77, we can redo the computation by substituting $\sum X = 84 + 86 + 65 + 77 = 312$ in the numerator and $n = 4$ in the denominator:

$$\overline{X} = \frac{\sum X}{n} = \frac{84 + 86 + 65 + 77}{4} = \frac{312}{4} = 78$$

As we can see, the formula for computing the average is quite simple when the values are all worth (or weighted) the same. If the weights are different, then we must take those weights into account to accurately compute the average.

Example:

A student takes 4 exams and wants to find their average grade. All tests have different weights in this class. According to the professor's syllabus: Tests 1 and 2 are worth 15% each, Test 3 is worth 30%, and Test 4 is worth 40% of the semester grade. Test grades are: 84, 86, 65, 77.

To account for the different percentages, we multiply the percentage of each score times the score itself and find the sum of those products. *Note: Remember to convert the percentages to decimal form.*

$$(0.15)84 + (0.15)86 + (0.30)65 + (0.40)77 = 75.8$$

Another option is to convert the percentages to fractions.

$$\left(\frac{15}{100}\right)84 + \left(\frac{15}{100}\right)86 + \left(\frac{30}{100}\right)65 + \left(\frac{40}{100}\right)77 = 75.8$$

Using this last approach, we can see that all fractions are out of 100. As such we can rewrite the sum as follows:

$$\frac{15(84)}{100} + \frac{15(86)}{100} + \frac{30(65)}{100} + \frac{40(77)}{100}$$

Since the total is out of 100, we say $n = 100$. However, since the test scores are weighed differently, we can add up the X values and divide by n. We need to multiply the weight (or frequency) value, add up those products and divide by 100.

The formula $\overline{X} = \dfrac{\sum X}{n}$ is modifies to account for each weight w. The weighted average (or mean formula is $\overline{X} = \dfrac{\sum w \cdot X}{n}$. Since n is the total of all weights (or frequencies), $n = \sum w$.

So, replacing n in the formula, we obtain the following formula used in statistics.

$$\overline{X} = \frac{\sum w \cdot X}{\sum w} \text{ when using } w \text{ for weights.}$$

Using f for each frequency value (representing the weights), we modify the formula and obtain to following formula.

$$\overline{X} = \frac{\sum f \cdot X}{\sum f} \text{ or } \frac{\sum f \cdot X}{n} \text{ when using } f \text{ for the weights.}$$

This last formula is used when computing the average or mean for a given frequency table, in which the X values are listed in one column and each frequency value is listed in another column.

Example:

a. A college student was enrolled in four classes: Math, English, Chemistry, and French. The credit weights are as follows: Math is 5 credits, English is 3 credits,

54

Chemistry is 3 credits, and French is 4 credits. The student's grades at the end of the semester are summarized in the following table:

	Grade	Number of Credits
Math	A	5
English	B	3
Chemistry	C	3
French	D	4

To compute the student's semester average, we need to convert the letter grades to numerical values on the 4.0 scale, where A = 4, B =3, C =2, D = 1 and F= 0. Each grade is X and the number of course credit hours is w.

	Grade X	Number of Credits w
Math	4	5
English	3	3
Chemistry	2	3
French	1	4

X	w	$w \cdot X$
4	5	20
3	3	9
2	3	6
1	4	5

$$\sum w = 15 \qquad\qquad \sum w \cdot X = 39$$

Substitute those values in the formula: $\overline{X} = \dfrac{\sum w \cdot X}{\sum w} = \dfrac{39}{15} = 2.6$

So, the student's grade point average (GPA) for the semester is 2.6.

If the courses had the same credit hours each, we could compute the average using the same approach we just used above with the new credit hours under the w column. However, we would have also the option of using the first formula and just find the $\sum X$ divided by n which can be expressed as the fraction $\dfrac{\sum X}{n}$. In this approach n would represent the number of courses and not the sum of the credit hours since we will not weigh in the number of credits.

b. Using the same grades from the previous case, we modify the credits so that each course was a 3 credit hours course.

	Grade	Number of Credits
Math	A	3
English	B	3
Chemistry	C	3
French	D	3

	Grade X	Number of Credits w
Math	4	3
English	3	3
Chemistry	2	3
French	1	3

Let's compare the two methods: $\overline{X} = \dfrac{\sum w \cdot X}{\sum w}$ versus $\overline{X} = \dfrac{\sum X}{n}$

Method 1: Using the formula $\overline{X} = \dfrac{\sum w \cdot X}{\sum w}$

X	w	$w \cdot X$
4	3	12
3	3	9
2	3	6
1	3	3

$$\sum w = 12 \qquad\qquad \sum w \cdot X = 30$$

Substitute those values in the formula: $\overline{X} = \dfrac{\sum w \cdot X}{\sum w} = \dfrac{30}{12} = 2.5$

So the student's grade point average (GPA) for the semester is 2.5.

Method 2: Using the formula $\overline{X} = \dfrac{\sum X}{n}$

	Grade X	Number of Credits w
Math	4	3
English	3	3
Chemistry	2	3
French	1	3

$$\sum X = 10 \qquad n = 4 \ (4 \text{ courses}) \qquad \text{NOTE: } n \ne \sum w$$

Substitute those values in the formula: $\overline{X} = \dfrac{\sum X}{n} = \dfrac{10}{4} = 2.5$

So the student's grade point average (GPA) for the semester is 2.5.

c. Referring to the example in Chapter 2 Section 2-5, we are given the following:

A survey of 100 Statistics students was conducted to determine the average time in minutes it takes to complete their daily assignments. The results are given below in the following grouped frequency table in which the minutes are grouped into class intervals.

Find the average number of minutes spent on the assignments.

The number of minutes spent on the assignments	Number of Students (Frequency)
10 – 19	10
20 – 29	39
30 – 39	44
40 – 49	4
50 – 59	2
60 – 69	1

We then organized the table using the class midpoints in place of the original class limits.

The number of minutes spent on the assignments (Midpoints)	Number of Students (Frequency)
14.5	10
24.5	39
34.5	44
44.5	4
54.5	2
64.5	1

To compute the mean we use the weighted mean formula using each frequency f in place of w and each X is represented as X_m or the midpoint of each class. So the formula for the weighted mean of the grouped frequency distribution is

$$\overline{X} = \frac{\sum f \cdot X_m}{n}$$

X_m	f	$f \cdot X_m$
14.5	10	145
24.5	39	955.5
34.5	44	1518
44.5	4	178
54.5	2	109
64.5	1	64.5

$$n = 100 \qquad \sum f \cdot X_m = 2970$$

Substitute those values in the formula: $\overline{X} = \dfrac{\sum f \cdot X_m}{n} = \dfrac{2970}{100} = 29.7$

Your Turn to Practice

Find the average.

1. Find the average of the following numbers. 24, 55, 40, 15, 60, 23, 20, 49, 10, 52

2. A student is trying to compute her average in a class that consisted of 3 quizzes, a midterm, and a final. Her quiz grades are 86, 78, 79. Her grade on the midterm was a 72 and on the final a 64.

   The professor's syllabus states:

         Quizzes are each worth 10% of the semester grade

         Midterm is worth 30% of the semester grade

         Final Exam is worth 40% of the semester grade

   Compute her average in the class.

3. The given grouped frequency table represents the number of minutes 60 shoppers spent shopping on-line on a weekday. Find the class midpoints and class boundaries. Compute the average number of minutes shopping on-line.

The number of minutes shopping on-line	Number of people (Frequency)
0.0 – 10.4	10
10.5 – 20.9	19
21.0 – 31.4	11
31.5 – 41.9	8
42.0 – 52.4	9
52.5 – 62.9	1
63.0 – 73.4	2

3.4 Compute the Square Root

Compute s given the value of s^2

In Algebra, we use the square root property to solve equations with variable terms squared by taking the square root of both sides. We set up the equation with the variable or variable term squared on one side (typically the left) and the number on the other side (typically the right). To eliminate the square, we take the square root of both sides to "undo" the square. On the number side, we place the $\pm$ in front of the square root symbol to obtain both possible solutions. See the steps below to solve the given equation.

$$\left(variable\ expression\right)^2 = number$$

$$\sqrt{\left(variable\ expression\right)^2} = \pm\sqrt{number} \qquad \text{Take the square root of both sides.}$$

Place $\pm$ in front of square root of the number.

$$variable\ expression = \pm\sqrt{number} \qquad \text{Solve for the variable.}$$

Examples:

Solve for the given variable.

a. $x^2 = 25$

$$\sqrt{x^2} = \pm\sqrt{25}$$

$$x = \pm\sqrt{25}$$

$$x = \pm5$$

So the two solutions are $x = 5$ and $x = -5$

62

b. $x^2 = 48$

$$\sqrt{x^2} = \pm\sqrt{48}$$

$$x = \pm\sqrt{48}$$

$$x = \pm4\sqrt{3}$$

So, the two exact solutions are $x = 4\sqrt{3}$ and $x = -4\sqrt{3}$

The approximate solutions to the nearest tenths are $x \approx 6.9$ and $x \approx -6.9$

c. $(x+3)^2 = 49$

$$\sqrt{(x+3)^2} = \pm\sqrt{49}$$

$$x+3 = \pm\sqrt{49}$$

$$x+3 = \pm7$$

$$x = -3 \pm 7$$

$$x = -3+7 = 4 \qquad x = -3-7 = -10$$

So, the two solutions are $x = 4$ and $x = -10$

63

d. $(x-2)^2 = 89$

$$\sqrt{(x-2)^2} = \pm\sqrt{89}$$

$$x-2 = \pm\sqrt{89}$$

$$x = 2\pm\sqrt{89}$$

$$x = 2+\sqrt{89} \qquad x = 2-\sqrt{89}$$

So, the two exact solutions are $x = 2 + \sqrt{89}$ and $x = 2 - \sqrt{89}$

The approximate solutions to the nearest tenths are $x \approx 11.4$ and $x \approx -7.4$

e. $c^2 = a^2 + b^2$ Let $a = 5$ and $b = 12$ and c cannot be negative.

First, we substitute a and b and simplify. Then solve for c.

$$c^2 = (5)^2 + (12)^2$$
$$c^2 = 25 + 144$$

$$c^2 = 169$$

$$\sqrt{c^2} = \pm\sqrt{169}$$

$$c = \pm\sqrt{169}$$

$$c = \pm 13$$

So, the two solutions from the equation are $c = 13$ and $c = -13$. However, since c cannot be negative, the only solution is $c = 13$.

64

In this last example, we were given that c cannot be negative. There are applications in geometry and statistics where the variable is known to be a non-negative value. In this situation we would automatically disregard the negative solution. The last example can be applied in geometry using the Pythagorean Theorem to find the length of the hypotenuse of a right triangle given the lengths of the other two sides known as the legs. In that example, the lengths are as follows a and b represent the lengths of the two legs and c represents the length of the hypotenuse. Since we are working with lengths, c can never be negative.

In statistics, the standard deviation is also a measurement that can never be negative. Therefore when solving for s or σ given s^2 or σ^2, the solution is never negative.

Examples:

Solve for the given variable.

    a. $s^2 = 36$ where s represents the standard deviation of a sample

$$\sqrt{s^2} = \pm\sqrt{36}$$

$$s = \pm\sqrt{36}$$

$$s = \pm 6$$

So, the two solutions for the algebra equation are $s = 6$ and $s = -6$. However, since the standard deviation s cannot be negative, the only solution is $s = 6$.

We can also solve this equation, without inserting $\pm$ since the negative solution is impossible.

$$s^2 = 36$$
$$\sqrt{s^2} = \sqrt{36}$$
$$s = \sqrt{36}$$
$$s = 6$$

So, the solution is $s = 6$.

b. $\sigma^2 = 63$ where σ represents the standard deviation of the population

$$\sqrt{\sigma^2} = \sqrt{63}$$

$$\sigma = \sqrt{63}$$

$$\sigma = 3\sqrt{7}$$

So, the exact solution is $\sigma = 3\sqrt{7}$.

The approximate solution to the nearest tenths is $\sigma \approx 7.9$

Your Turn to Practice

Solve for the given variable.

1. $n^2 = 100$

2. $\left(x-5\right)^2 = 81$

3. $y^2 = 50$

4. $\sigma^2 = 16$ where σ represents the standard deviation of the population

5. $s^2 = 9$ where s represents the standard deviation of a sample

6. $s^2 = 84$ where s represents the standard deviation of a sample

3.5 Define and Apply the Notation ± to Apply the Empirical Rule

In statistics, we apply the Empirical Rule (also known as the 68-95-99.7 Rule) to normally distributed (bell-shaped) data.

According to the Empirical Rule:

- Approximately 68% of the data values will fall within 1 standard deviation of the mean.
- Approximately 95% of the data values will fall within 2 standard deviations of the mean.
- Approximately 99.7% of the data values will fall within 3 standard deviations of the mean.

For a sample, using the notations $\overline{X}$ and s, we can restate the Empirical Rule as follows:

- Approximately 68% of the data values will fall within $\overline{X} \pm 1s$ in other words between $\overline{X} - 1s$ and $\overline{X} + 1s$.
- Approximately 95% of the data values will fall within $\overline{X} \pm 2s$ in other words between $\overline{X} - 2s$ and $\overline{X} + 2s$.
- Approximately 99.7% of the data values will fall within $\overline{X} \pm 3s$ in other words between $\overline{X} - 3s$ and $\overline{X} + 3s$.

Example:

In a sample of online gamers (people playing videos games online), the mean (or average) time spent playing online was 2 hours with a standard deviation of 15 minutes. Assuming the data is normally distributed, apply the Empirical Rule.

First, we convert 2 hours to 120 minutes so $\overline{X} = 120$ and $s = 15$. We substitute those values and get the following:

Approximately 68% of the data values will fall within $120 \pm 1(15)$ which is $120 - 1(15) = 105$ and $120 + 1(15) = 135$.

Approximately 95% of the data values will fall within $120 \pm 2(15)$ which is $120 - 2(15) = 90$ and $120 + 2(15) = 150$.

Approximately 99.7% of the data values will fall within $120 \pm 3(15)$ which is $120 - 3(15) = 75$ and $120 + 3(15) = 165$.

From the Empirical Rule, we conclude that approximately 68% of online gamers spend 105 to 135 minutes playing online. While, approximately 95% of online gamers spend 90 to 150 minutes playing online. Finally, approximately 99.7% of online gamers spend 75 to 165 minutes playing online.

Your Turn to Practice

Assuming the data is normally distributed, apply the Empirical Rule.

In a sample of 200 adults, their mean (or average) nighttime sleep was 6 hours with a standard deviation of 10 minutes.

3.6 Read and Interpret Box-Plots: Identify the Five-Number Summary

In statistics, the data set can be divided into four parts known as quartiles. To partition the data into two parts, we use the median. From the median, we further divide each half into two additional halves, one for the lower half of the data set and the other for the upper half of the data set. The numbers that separate the quartiles are known as Q_1, Q_2 and Q_3.

Q_1 separates the first and second quartiles.

Q_2 separates the second and third quartiles. NOTE: Q_2 is also the median.

Q_3 separates the third and fourth quartiles.

The corresponding graph when using quartiles is known as a boxplot. In a boxplot, we label Q_1, Q_2 (or median) and Q_3 along with the smallest and largest data values. These five numbers: Minimum, Q_1, Q_2 (or median),Q_3 and the Maximum can summarized as the five-number summary. When graphing a boxplot, the values Q_1, Q_2 (or median) and Q_3 are enclosed in a rectangle (or box). A line is then draw on each end of the rectangle connecting the box to the maximum and minimum values. See below.

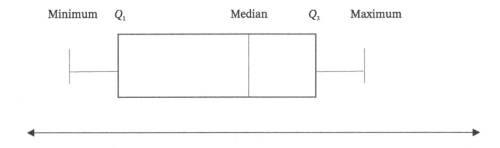

Minimum Q_1 Median Q_3 Maximum

70

Example:

The given data set represent the ages (in years) of evening students, use the boxplot to identify the five-number summary.

| 20 | 29 | 29 | 30 | 31 | 33 | 36 | 37 | 38 |
| 40 | 41 | 50 | 55 | 57 | 58 | 61 | 70 |

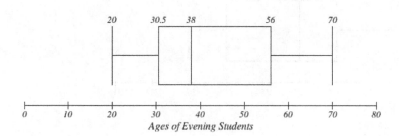
Ages of Evening Students

The minimum age plotted is 20 and the maximum age plotted is 70. The lowest value in the rectangle (or box) is 30.5, which is Q_1. The middle value in the box is 38, which is the median. The highest value in the rectangle (or box) is 56, which is Q_3.

The five-number summary is:

Minimum = 20 $Q_1 = 30.5$ Median = 38 $Q_3 = 56$ Maximum = 70

71

Your Turn to Practice

Use the boxplot to identify the five-number summary.

1. The following is a boxplot for the number of minutes a group of students spent commuting from their homes to school on a given week.

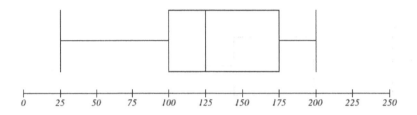

2. The following is a boxplot for the number of kilowatt hours used weekly in a typical household.

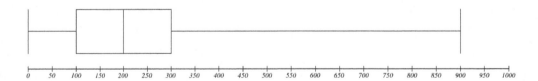

3. The following is a boxplot for the number of minutes another group of students spent commuting from their homes to school on a given week.

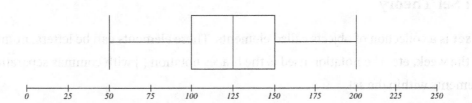

Chapter 4 Probability Skills

4.1 Set Theory

A **set** is a collection of objects called elements. These elements can be letters, numbers, days of the week, etc. The notation used is the braces notation { } with commas separating the elements within the set.

A set that contains no elements is called a **null set** or **empty set**. An empty set is represented with the braces with no element inside { } or as Ø. *NOTE: Either notation may be used, however {Ø} would be incorrect since the outer set is not empty.*

Examples:

Set A represents the set of counting numbers from 1 to 10

A = {1, 2, 3, 4, 5, 6, 7, 8, 9, 10}

Set B represents the set of 6 major U.S. wireless phone carriers

B = {AT&T, Verizon, T-Mobile, Sprint, MetroPCS, Boost}

Set C is an empty set.

C = { } or Ø.

A **subset** is a set containing the same or fewer elements of another set. Thus, a subset is a set entirely contained within another set.

The **Universal Set** represents the set of all elements possible in a particular experiment. In probability, we refer to the universal set as the **sample space**. Thus, the **sample space** is the set that contains all possible outcomes in a probability experiment.

For the remainder of this text, we will use the term sample space only, and set *S* will represent the sample space.

Example:

Let *S* represent the sample space of all counting numbers.

S = {1, 2, 3, 4, 5, 6, 7, 8, 9, 10, 11, 12, 13,...}

From the previous example A = {1, 2, 3, 4, 5, 6, 7, 8, 9, 10}. We observe that all of the elements of A are contained in the sample space *S*. Therefore, A is a subset of *S*.

We define the **complement** of a set as the set containing the elements that are NOT in the given set but are in the remainder of the sample space. The complement of a set E, can be denoted as Ē, E′ or E^c.

Example:

$$S = \{1, 2, 3, 4, 5, 6, 7, 8, 9, 10, 11, 12, 13,...\}$$

If A = {1, 2, 3, 4, 5, 6, 7, 8, 9, 10}, then to find the complement of A, we remove those elements from the sample space and the complement is the set with the rest of the elements Ā = {11, 12, 13,...}. We will denote the complement of an event by adding a bar above the event name. In this case, the complement of event A is Ā.

Examples:

a. Set *S* represents the sample space for all the days in a non-leap year. *For most probabilities, we assume non-leap years. In other words, there are only 28 days in February, thus 365 days in a year.*

$$S = \{\text{January 1, January 2, January 3,..., February 28, March 1, March 2,...,}$$
$$\text{December 31}\}$$

b. Set S represents the sample space for a single coin toss.

$$S = \{\text{Heads, Tails}\} \text{ or } \{H, T\}$$

c. Set S represents the sample space for the roll of a six-sided die.

$$S = \{1, 2, 3, 4, 5, 6\}$$

d. Set S represents the sample space for the roll of a pair of dice. Each pair represents the outcomes for the two dice. We can call each Die 1 and Die 2 and the pair (Die 1 outcome, Die 2 outcome).

$$S = \{(1,1), (1, 2), (1, 3), (1, 4), (1, 5), (1, 6)$$
$$(2,1), (2, 2), (2, 3), (2, 4), (2, 5), (2, 6)$$
$$(3,1), (3, 2), (3, 3), (3, 4), (3, 5), (3, 6)$$
$$(4,1), (4, 2), (4, 3), (4, 4), (4, 5), (4, 6)$$
$$(5,1), (5, 2), (5, 3), (5, 4), (5, 5), (5, 6)$$
$$(6,1), (6, 2), (6, 3), (6, 4), (6, 5), (6, 6)\}$$

From S, we can define the subset B as the set of possibilities of rolling a sum of 5 from the pair of dice *(sum of the two dice is 5)*.

B = {(1, 4), (2, 3), (3, 2), (4, 1)}

From *S*, we can define the subset C as the set of possibilities of rolling a sum of 1 from the pair of dice *(sum of the two dice is 1)*.

C = { } or Ø since it is impossible to roll a sum equal to 1. The smallest sum is a 2.

Your Turn to Practice

1. We are given S = {a, b, c, d, e, f, g, h} and R = {e, f, g}. Find the complement of R.

2. We are given that the sample space is the set of the seven days of the week and T = {Saturday, Sunday}. Find the complement of T.

3. We are given that the sample space is the set of all possible outcomes in a roll of six-sided die and event E is rolling a number less than 3. Find the complement of E.

4. Find the sample space for two coin tosses. List each outcome as an ordered pair.

5. Find the sample space for three coin tosses. List each outcome as an ordered pair.

6. A spinner consists of four options 0, 1, 2, 3 (see below). The spinner is spun twice. Find the sample space by listing all possible pairs. In other words, list each outcome as an ordered pair (Spin 1 outcome, Spin 2 outcome).

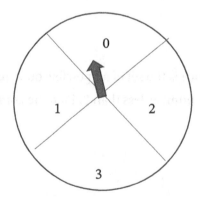

Sets that do not have any elements in common are defined as **mutually exclusive** sets.   In probability, events that cannot occur at the same time or have no common occurrence are also called mutually exclusive (or disjoint) events.   Below is a Venn diagram for a pair of mutually exclusive sets A and B.   The rectangle represents the sample space, and each circle represents an event.

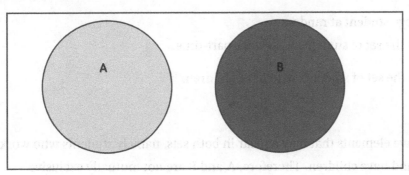

Examples:

Determine whether these sets are mutually exclusive.

   a.   Roll a six-sided die.

        A is the set of numbers rolled that are greater than 2.   A = {3, 4, 5, 6}

        B is the set of numbers rolled that are even.   B = {2, 4, 6}

        A and B have elements that appear in both sets, namely 4 and 6.   Therefore, A and B are not mutually exclusive.

   b.   Roll a six-sided die.

        C is the set of numbers rolled that are greater than 2.   C = {3, 4, 5, 6}

        D is the set of numbers rolled that are at most 2 *(at most means less than or equal to}.*

        D = {1, 2}

C and D have no elements that appear in both sets. Therefore, C and D are mutually exclusive

c. Pick a college student at random.

A is the set of students who work part-time.

B is the set of students who have children.

A and B have elements that may appear in both sets, namely students who work part-time and have children. Therefore, A and B are not mutually exclusive.

The **intersection** of two sets is the set containing all elements common to BOTH sets. If there are no elements in common, the intersection is the empty set. In other words, when sets are mutually exclusive, the intersection of the two is the empty set.

Notation for the intersection of sets A **and** B is $A \cap B$. Note the emphasis on the word **AND**, since both must be satisfied.

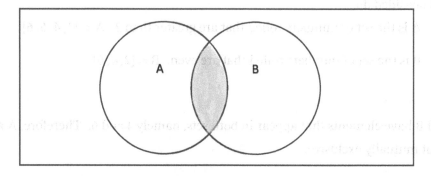

The **union** of two sets is the set containing elements from either set **or** from BOTH sets. The union contains elements that are found in **at least one** of the two sets.

Notation for the intersection of sets A **or** B is $A \cup B$. Note the emphasis on the word **OR**, since either A or B or both must be satisfied.

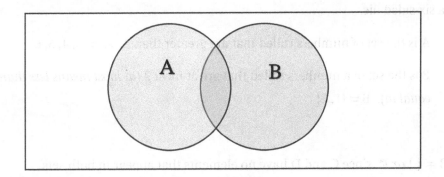

Examples:

Find the intersection and union of the pairs of sets given.

   a. Roll a six-sided die.

        A is the set of numbers rolled that are greater than 2. A = {3, 4, 5, 6}

        B is the set of a numbers rolled that are even. B = {2, 4, 6}

        $A \cap B = \{4, 6\}$ since elements 4 and 6 appear in both sets.

        $A \cup B = \{2, 3, 4, 5, 6\}$ since elements 2, 3, 4, 5 and 6 appear in at least one of the two sets.

   b. Pick a college student at random.

        C is the set of students who work part-time.

        D is the set of students who have children.

        $C \cap D =$ the set of students who both work part-time and have children.

        $C \cap D =$ the set of students who either work part-time or have children or both.

81

c. Roll a six-sided die.

A is the set of numbers rolled that are greater than 2. A = {3, 4, 5, 6}

B is the set of a numbers rolled that are at most 2 (*at most means less than or equal to*). B = {1, 2}

A ∩ B = { } *or* ∅ since C and D have no elements that appear in both sets.

A ∪ B = {1, 2, 3, 4, 5, 6} since elements 1, 2, 3, 4, 5 and 6 appear in at least one of the two sets.

Your Turn to Practice

Determine whether these sets are mutually exclusive. Write YES if they are mutually exclusive or NO if they are not mutually exclusive.

1. Roll a six-sided die.

   A is the set of numbers rolled that are greater than 4.

   B is the set of numbers rolled that are odd.

2. Pick a college student at random.
   A is the set of students who work full-time.

   B is the set of students who smoke.

3. Flip a coin.

   C is the outcome of getting TAILS

D is the outcome of getting HEADS

4. Pick a college student at random.

     A is the set of students who work full-time.

     B is the set of students who smoke.

Find the intersection and union of the given sets for Questions 5-11.

    A = {a, b, x, y, z}   B = {a, g, h, j, w, y}   C = {c, d, e, f, g, h}

5. Find A ∩ B

6. Find A ∪ B

7. Find A ∩ C

8. Find A ∪ C

9. Find B ∩ C

10. Find B ∪ C

11. Find A ∩ B ∩ C

12. Roll a six-sided die. A is the set of numbers rolled that are greater than 4. B is the set of numbers rolled that are odd. Find A ∩ B and A ∪ B.

13. Flip a coin. C is the outcome of getting TAILS. D is the outcome of getting HEADS. Find C ∩ D and C ∪ D.

14. Pick a college student at random. A is the set of students who work full-time. B is the set of students who smoke. Describe in words A ∩ B and A ∪ B

4.2 Add/Subtract Fractions and Decimals to Compute Probability of the Complement of an Event

The probability of an event plus the probability of the complement of the event equals 100% or 1.

$$P(E) + P(\overline{E}) = 100\% \quad \text{or} \quad P(E) + P(\overline{E}) = 1$$

Examples:

a. Let A represent an event with a 20% chance or a probability of 20%. Find the probability that event A will NOT occur.

In percentage form:

Since $P(A) = 20\%$ then the probability of the complement of A or $P(\overline{A}) = 100\% - 20\%$

$$= 80\%$$

∴ $P(not\ A) = 80\%$ NOTE: *Symbol* ∴ *means therefore.*

<u>In decimal form</u>, convert 20% to 0.20.

Since P(A) = 0.20, the probability of the complement of A or $P(\overline{A}) = 1 - 0.20$

$$= 0.80$$

$\therefore P(not\ A) = 0.80$

<u>In fraction form</u>, convert 20% to $= \frac{20}{100} = \frac{1}{5}$

Since $P(A) = \frac{1}{5}$, the probability of the complement of A or $P(\overline{A}) = 1 - \frac{1}{5}$

$$= \frac{5}{5} - \frac{1}{5}$$

$$= \frac{4}{5}$$

$\therefore P(not\ A) = \frac{4}{5}$

b. Set S represents the sample space for the roll of a six-sided die.

$S = \{1, 2, 3, 4, 5, 6\}$. The number of outcomes in S is 6.

Let E be the event that we obtain a number less than 3.   Therefore, set E = {1, 2}.

So the number of outcomes in E is 2.

Then the probability of E or $P(E) = \frac{2}{6} = \frac{1}{3}$

To find the probability that the event E *does not* occur or the complement of E, we subtract the probability of E from 1. In other words,

$$P(\overline{E}) = 1 - \frac{1}{3}$$

$$= \frac{3}{3} - \frac{1}{3}$$

$$= \frac{2}{3}$$

$\therefore P(\textit{not } E) = \frac{2}{3}$

We can also verify this by finding the set $\overline{E}$.

Since set $E = \{1, 2\}$, set $\overline{E} = \{3, 4, 5, 6\}$. So the number of outcomes in $\overline{E}$ is 4.

Then the probability of $\overline{E}$ or $P(\overline{E}) = \frac{4}{6} = \frac{2}{3}$

In this example the sample space and the sets E and $\overline{E}$ were small, so finding $\overline{E}$ first was quick and easy. However, in many other probability examples, it would not be feasible to write out the complement of the given set, but the probability can still be computed quickly using the fact that $P(\overline{E}) = 1 - P(E)$.

c. Let B represent an event with probability 0.847. Find the probability that event B will NOT occur.

Since $P(B) = 0.847$, the probability of the complement of B or $P(\overline{B}) = 1 - 0.847$

$$= 0.153$$

$\therefore P(\textit{not } B) = 0.153$

d. Set S represents the sample space for all the days in a non-leap year.

$S = \{$January 1, January 2, January 3,..., February 28, March 1, March 2,..., December 31$\}$. So the number of outcomes in S is 365.

Let E represent the set of all the days in July.

$E = \{$July 1, July 2, July 3, July 4,..., July 31$\}$. So the number of outcomes in E is 31.

Then the probability of E or $P(E) = \frac{31}{365}$

To find the probability that event E does not occur or the complement of E, we subtract the probability of X from 1. In other words,

$$P(\overline{E}) = 1 - \frac{31}{365}$$

$$= \frac{365}{365} - \frac{31}{365}$$

$$= \frac{334}{365}$$

$$\therefore P(\text{not E}) = \frac{334}{365}$$

Your Turn to Practice

1. Let A represent an event with a probability of 35%. Find the probability that event A will NOT occur.

2. Let B represent an event with a probability of 98.9%. Find the probability that event B will NOT occur.

3. Let C represent an event with probability 0.726. Find the probability that event C will NOT occur.

4. Let D represent an event with a probability of 0.0000012. Find the probability that event D will NOT occur.

5. Given $S = \{a, b, c, d, e, f, g, h\}$ and $R = \{e, f, g\}$. Each of the outcomes in S are equally likely. Find $P(R)$ and $P(\overline{R})$.

6. Set S represents the sample space for all the days in a non-leap year. Let A represent the set of all the days in February. Find the probability that event A will NOT occur.

4.3 Relate Percentages to Probabilities

The probability of an event is the chance or likelihood that the event will occur.

If we know that there is a 100% chance of an event taking place, then the probability of that event is 100% and its probability is 1. In other words, that event will always occur.

If we know that there is a 0% chance of an event taking place, then the probability of that event is 0% and its probability is 0. In other words, that event will never occur.

Any percentage in between 0% and 100%, means that the event may or may not occur. The closer the percentage is to 100%, the higher the chance that the event happens. On the other hand, the closer the percentage is to 0%, the smaller the chance that the event happens.

Therefore, we say that the probability of any event is always between and including 0% and 100%.

It is impossible for a probability to be higher than 100%, although in other math applications we could have more than 100% (for example, a 200% price increase).

The probability of an event E cannot be negative or greater than 100%.

$$0\% \leq P(E) \leq 100\% \quad [\text{In decimal form, } 0 \leq P(E) \leq 1]$$

Example:

Determine how likely the occurrence of the given event is.

Classify the event as: **Will never occur, Low chance, The same chance to occur or not occur, High chance, Will always occur**

a. $P(A) = 100\%$.

Since the percentage is 100%, Event A: **Will always occur**

b. $P(B) = 0\%$.

Since the percentage is 0%, Event B: **Will never occur**

c. $P(C) = 50\%$.

Since the percentage is 50%, Event C: **The same chance to occur or not occur**

d. $P(A) = 85\%$.

Since the percentage is 85%, Event A: **High chance**

e. $P(B) = 33\%$.

Since the percentage is 33%, Event B: **Low chance**

Your Turn to Practice

Determine how likely the given event is to occur.

Classify the event as:

Will never occur, Low chance, The same chance to occur or not occur, High chance, Will always occur

1. $P(L) = 21\%$. Event L:

2. $P(H) = 50\%$. Event H:

3. $P(F) = 100\%$. Event F:

4. $P(K) = 92\%$. Event K:

5. $P(G) = 0\%$. Event G:

4.4 Applying Significant Figures and Using Scientific Notation for Probabilities

We defined significant digits (or figures) in Chapter 2. In this section we apply significant digits to probabilities expressed in decimal form. When the probability value in decimal form needs to be rounded, the number may be rounded to two, three or four significant digits, although more may be used. It is important to note that there is no set rule of the number of significant digits used.

Example:

In Section 4.4.2 Example 4, we computed the probability of selecting a day in the month of July.

Let E represent the number of days in July.

E = {July 1, July 2, July 3, July 4,..., July 31}. Thus, the number of outcomes in E is 31.

Then the probability of E or $P(E) = \frac{31}{365}$. If we wish to express this in decimal form, we get approximately from the calculator display 0.915068493 which can be rounded off to either two or three significant figures.

If we round to two significant figures, the second significant figure is the digit 1 which is followed by a 5 so the 1 gets rounded up to 2. Therefore, 0.91506843 ≈ 0.92 when rounded to two significant digits.

If we round to three significant figures, the third significant figure is the digit 5 which is followed by a 0 so the 5 does not get rounded up. Therefore, 0.91506843 ≈ 0.915 when rounded to three significant digits.

In the event, that we wish to round to more significant figures, we apply the same approach. If we choose to round to four significant figures, the fourth significant figure is the digit 0 which is followed by a 6 so the so the 0 gets rounded up to 1. Therefore, 0.91506843 ≈ 0.9151 when rounded to four significant digits.

Your Turn to Practice

Compute the following probabilities.

Express your answer in decimal form.

    a) Round to two significant figures
    b) Round to three significant figures
 1. Find the probability that a randomly selected person's birthday is in February.

2. Find the probability of rolling a six-sided die, and getting a 2.

3. Find the probability of not winning a prize, if the probability of winning the prize is $\frac{5}{187954}$.

Scientific notation is another way of expressing a number. For very large or very small values with a lot of place values, it is more practical than writing the entire number out. The answer is left in a more compressed, easy to read form.

The general form for scientific notation is $N \times 10^{exponent}$ where N is a number greater than or equal to 1.0 and less than 10. In other words, $1.0 \leq N < 10$. The number in the ones place ranges between 1 and 9 usually followed by two decimal places after the decimal point. Note: It is possible to use only 1 decimal place, but typically we use 2 decimal places.

To write a number in scientific notation $N \times 10^{exponent}$, move the decimal after the first non-zero digit and then count the number of spaces that the decimal was moved to determine the value of the exponent.

To determine the sign of the exponent of base 10, use the following:

If the original number is **greater than 1**, the exponent of base 10 will be positive.

If the original number is **less than 1**, the exponent of base 10 will be negative.

Examples:

Express the following numbers in scientific notation.

    a. 1,458

> Since the original number is greater than 1, the exponent on base 10 will be a positive number. The decimal is at the end of 1458, first move it three places the left after the first significant digit which is 1 to get 1.458. To leave it with two decimal places, we round the number to 1.46 so we get 1.46×10^3.

    b. 23.1429

> Since the original number is greater than 1, the exponent on base 10 will be a positive number. The decimal is between 3 and 1, first move it one place the left after the first significant digit which is 2 to get 2.31429. To leave it with two decimal places, we round the number to 2.31 so we get 2.31×10^1.

    c. 0.02287

> Since the original number is less than 1, the exponent on base 10 will be a negative number. The decimal is in front of the zero in the ones place, first move it two places to the right after the first significant digit which is the first 2 to get 2.287. To leave it with two decimal places, we round the number to 2.29 so we get 2.29×10^{-2}.

    d. 0.05

> Since the original number is less than 1, the exponent on base 10 will be a negative number. The decimal is in front of the zero in the ones place, first move it two places to the right after the first significant digit which is the 5 to get 5 or 5.0. To leave it with two decimal places, we add more zeros after the decimal point so we get 5.00×10^{-2}.

e. 0.00039984

Since the original number is less than 1, the exponent on base 10 will be a negative number. The decimal is in front of the zero in the ones place, first move it four places to the right after the first significant digit which is the first 3 to get 3.9984. To leave it with two decimal places, we round the number to 4.00 so we get 4.00×10^{-4}.

f. 0.00000005943

Since the original number is less than 1, the exponent on base 10 will be a negative number. The decimal is in front of the zero in the ones place, first move it eight places to the right after the first non-zero digit which is the 5 to get 5.943. To leave it with two decimal places, we round the number to 5.94 so we get 5.94×10^{-8}.

Your Turn to Practice

Express the following numbers in scientific notation.

1. 5,867

2. 0.000499899

3. 76.71839

4. 0.0841914

5. 143,884

6. 0.0375

7. 0.07

8. 0.00000004673855

To convert the number from scientific notation back to decimal form, move the decimal point to the left or right depending on the sign of the exponent of base 10.

If the sign of the exponent is positive, move the decimal to the right.

If the sign of the exponent is negative, move the decimal to the left.

Examples:

Convert the following numbers from scientific notation to decimal form.

96

a. 8.36×10^2

> Since the sign of the exponent is positive, we move the decimal two places to the right, so the answer is 836 in decimal form.

b. 7.91×10^6

> Since the sign of the exponent is positive, we move the decimal six places to the right, so the answer is 7,910,000 in decimal form.

c. 3.28×10^{-1}

> Since the sign of the exponent is negative, we move the decimal one place to the left, so the answer is 0.328 in decimal form.

d. 6.57×10^{-3}

> Since the sign of the exponent is negative, we move the decimal three places to the left, so the answer is 0.00657 in decimal form.

e. 9.03×10^{-8}

> Since the sign of the exponent is negative, we move the decimal eight places to the left, so the answer is 0.0000000903 in decimal form.

Your Turn to Practice

Convert the following number from scientific notation to decimal form.

1. 4.59×10^3

97

2. 8.74×10^{-2}

3. 1.28×10^{-6}

4. 6.52×10^{4}

5. 9.59×10^{-1}

For probabilities, since the values cannot be greater than 1, we only apply scientific notation to decimal values between 0 and 1.

We can leave answers in reduced fraction form, decimal form or scientific notation. Scientific notation is useful small probability values that would require more zeros between the decimal point and the first significant digit. In the example below, we can see when scientific notation would be beneficial.

Examples:

Express the following probabilities in decimal form and in scientific notation.

   a. Toss a coin. Event A: Obtain Tails. Find P(A)

      $P(A) = \frac{1}{2}$

      In decimal form: $P(A) = 0.5$

      In scientific notation: $P(A) = 5.00 \times 10^{-1}$

   b. Roll a six-sided die. Event B: Obtain a number greater than 4. Find P(B)

      $P(B) = \frac{2}{3}$

98

In decimal form: $P(B) = 0.666666\cdots \approx 0.667$(three significant figures)

In scientific notation: $P(B) = 6.67 \times 10^{-1}$

c. Consider a non-leap year. Event C: Someone randomly selected was born on 4th of July. Find $P(C)$.

$P(C) = \frac{1}{365}$

In decimal form: $P(C) = 0.002739726 \approx 0.003$(three significant figures)

In scientific notation: $P(C) = 2.74 \times 10^{-3}$

For these three cases, we can see that in parts (a) and (b), it was better to express the answer in the original fraction form or in standard decimal form. However in part (c), it was better to express the answer in the original fraction or in scientific notation because the rounded number in scientific notation is a bit more precise.

Your Turn to Practice

Express the following probabilities from the previous exercises in decimal form using three significant figures and in scientific notation.

1. Find the probability that a randomly selected person's birthday is in February.

2. Find the probability of not winning a prize, if the probability of winning the prize is $\frac{5}{187954}$.

3. Find the probability of rolling a six-sided die and getting a 2.

4.5 Compute Ratios and Define the Odds For/Against

Ratios are fractions that can be expressed in three forms: **Fraction form**, using the word **to**, using the colon : symbol.

We can write the ratio of for every a parts there are b as $\frac{a}{b}$, a to b, a :b

Examples:

Express the following as a ratio in all three forms.

a. Write the ratio of "for every 3 parts there are 5."

   Either as $\frac{3}{5}$ or 3 to 5   or 3:5

b. Write the ratio of "for every 7 parts there are 2."

   Either as $\frac{7}{2}$ or 7 to 2   or 7:2

c. Write the ratio of "for every 6 parts there are 6."

   Either as $\frac{6}{6}$ or 6 to 6   or 6:6

   Since the fraction $\frac{6}{6}$ can be reduced to $\frac{1}{1}$, we can also express this ratio as

   Either as $\frac{1}{1}$ or 1 to 1 or 1:1

   In other words, a 6 to 6 ratio is the same as a 1 to 1 ratio.

Your Turn to Practice

Express the following as a ratio in all three forms.

1. Write the ratio of "for every 10 parts there are 10."

2. Write the ratio of "for every 4 parts there are 9."

3. Write the ratio of "for every 17 parts there are 3."

In probability applications, ratios are also used to represent the odds favoring or against an event. However, it is important to note the odds are NOT probabilities. Odds are related to probabilities, but they are not the same thing. Odds can be larger than 1 whereas probability values can never be more than 1.

Example:

Event E has 5 possibilities while Event E not occurring has 19 possibilities. Therefore, the total number of possible outcomes is 24.

So the probability favoring E or $P(E) = \frac{5}{24}$ and then the probability against E or $P(\overline{E}) = \frac{19}{24}$

The odds favoring E would be the 5 times favoring E to the 19 times against E. In other words, the odds favoring E are 5:19.

The odds against E would be the 19 times against E to the 5 times favoring E. In other words, the odds against E are 19:5. In fraction form $\frac{19}{5}$, the fraction for the odds is greater than one which is and impossible value for a probability.

Your Turn to Practice

1. Event A has 23 possibilities while Event A not occurring has 40 possibilities. Find the odds for and against Event A.

2. Event B has 8 possibilities of occurring. The total number of possibilities is 17. Find the odds for and against Event B.

3. Set S represents the sample space for the roll of a six-sided die. $S = \{1, 2, 3, 4, 5, 6\}$. Event C is to roll a number greater than 4. Find the odds for and against Event C.

4. Set S represents the sample space for the roll of a six-sided die. $S = \{1, 2, 3, 4, 5, 6\}$ Event D is to roll an odd number. Find the odds for and against Event D.

4.6 Using Algebra to Solve for the Conditional Probability

We use basic algebra in many probability applications. Algebraically, if we have an equation with three variables and we are given the values for two variables, we can solve for third variable. Likewise, in a probability formula with three probabilities and we are given two probability values, we can solve the equation and find the third probability value. One of these applications is finding the conditional probability for dependent events where we are provided two probability values: the probability of *one the events occurring* along with the probability of *one event* AND *the other event occurring*.

Basic Review of Algebra, where we solve for the given variable.

Examples:

Solve for x.

a. $5x = 10$ — Divide both sides by 5

$$\frac{5x}{5} = \frac{10}{5}$$

$$x = 2$$

b. $12x = 15$ — Divide both sides by 12

$$\frac{12x}{12} = \frac{15}{12}$$

$$x = \frac{5}{4}$$

c. $\frac{3}{4}x = \frac{15}{32}$ — Divide both sides by $\frac{3}{4}$

$$\frac{\frac{3}{4}x}{\frac{3}{4}} = \frac{\frac{15}{32}}{\frac{3}{4}}$$

$$\frac{4}{3} \cdot \frac{3}{4}x = \frac{4}{3} \cdot \frac{15}{32}$$ Multiply both sides by the reciprocal $\frac{4}{3}$

$$x = \frac{5}{8}$$

d. $0.24x = 0.072$ Divide both sides by 0.24

$$\frac{0.24x}{0.24} = \frac{0.072}{0.24}$$

$$x = 0.3$$

Your Turn to Practice

Solve for x.

1. $14x = 42$

2. $0.6x = 0.096$

3. $16x = 56$

4. $\frac{49}{81}x = \frac{14}{27}$

For conditional probability, if we are given the values of P(A and B), P(A), and P(B), we can use the formula for dependent events A and B to find the conditional probabilities P(A|B) and P(B|A).

NOTE: P(A|B) does not mean P(A) divided by P(B). P(A|B) means the probability that event A occurs GIVEN that event B occurs.

The formulas for Events A and B, when A and B are dependent are:

$$P(A \text{ and } B) = P(A)\, P(B|A)$$

$$P(A \text{ and } B) = P(B)\, P(A|B)$$

Example:

For dependent events A and B, P(A and B) = 0.056, P(A) = 0.8 P(B) = 0.28. Find P(A|B) and P(B|A).

$$P(A \text{ and } B) = P(A)\, P(B|A)$$

Substitute the values P(A and B) = 0.056 and P(A) = 0.8 and solve for P(B|A) algebraically.

Solving for P(B|A)

$0.056 = 0.8P(B|A)$ Use the same approach as solving for x in the equation. $0.056 = 0.8x$

$0.056 = 0.8P(B\|A)$	$0.056 = 0.8x$
$\dfrac{0.056}{0.8} = \dfrac{0.8P(B\|A)}{0.8}$ Divide both sides by 0.8	$\dfrac{0.056}{0.8} = \dfrac{0.8x}{0.8}$
$0.07 = P(B\|A)$	$0.07 = x$

Similarly, when solving for P(A|B)

$$P(A \text{ and } B) = P(B)\, P(A|B)$$

Substitute the values P(A and B) = 0.056 and P(B) = 0.28 and solve for P(A|B) algebraically.

Solving for P(A|B)

$0.056 = 0.28 P(A|B)$ Use the same approach as solving for x in the equation. $0.056 = 0.28x$

$0.056 = 0.28 P(A|B)$ $\qquad\qquad\qquad 0.056 = 0.28x$

$\dfrac{0.056}{0.28} = \dfrac{0.28 P(A|B)}{0.28}$ Divide both sides by 0.28 $\dfrac{0.056}{0.28} = \dfrac{0.28x}{0.28}$

$0.2 = P(A|B)$ $\qquad\qquad\qquad\qquad 0.2 = x$

<u>Your Turn to Practice</u>

1. Consider dependent events C and D.

   P(C and D) = 0.018,   P(C) = 0.3,   P(D) = 0.5.   Find P(C|D) and P(C|D).

2. Consider dependent events E and F.

   P(E and F) = 0.072, P(E) = 0.06, P(F) = 0.09. Find P(F|E).

3. Consider dependent events A and B.

   P(A and B) = 0.036, P(A) = 0.12, P(B) = 0.4. Find P(A|B).

4.7 Define Factorial, Combinations, and Permutations

We can use the factorial symbol to represent the product of all whole numbers from the given number in decreasing order down to 1. If we let n represent any natural (or counting) number then

$$n! = n(n-1)(n-2) \cdots 1.$$

In additional to the natural numbers, $n!$ is also defined when $n = 0$. 0! is defined as 1. We can think of 0! as the number of ways of arranging the elements in an empty set. Since the empty or null set has no elements, there is only 1 way of choosing an arrangement.

NOTE: If n is negative, the factorial is undefined.

Examples:

108

Compute the following. If necessary, leave the answer in scientific notation.

a. 3!

$$3! = (3)(2)(1)$$

$$= 6$$

b. 5!

$$5! = (5)(4)(3)(2)(1)$$

$$= 120$$

c. $(10 - 6)!$

$$(10 - 6)! = 4!$$

$$4! = (4)(3)(2)(1)$$

$$= 24$$

d. 15!

Using the calculator, we get $1.3076764360 \times 10^{12} \approx 1.31 \times 10^{12}$

e. $\dfrac{100!}{99!}$

The calculator cannot compute such high numbers like 100! or 99! We use the definition of the factorial to expand each factorial and then cancel out the common factor.

$$\frac{100!}{99!} = \frac{100(99)(98)(97)\cdots 1}{(99)(98)(97)\cdots 1}$$

$$= \frac{100}{1}$$

109

$$= 100$$

f. $\dfrac{105!}{103!}$

The calculator cannot compute such high numbers like 105! or 103! We use the definition of the factorial to expand each factorial and then cancel out the common factor.

$$\frac{105!}{103!} = \frac{105(104)(103)(102)(101)\cdots 1}{(103)(102)(101)\cdots 1}$$

$$= \frac{105(104)}{1}$$

$$= 10{,}920$$

g. $\dfrac{(n+1)!}{n!}$

We use the definition of the factorial to expand each factorial and then cancel out the common factor.

$$\frac{(n+1)!}{n!} = \frac{(n+1)(n)(n-1)(n-2)\cdots 1}{(n)(n-1)(n-2)\cdots 1}$$

$$= \frac{(n+1)}{1}$$

$$= n + 1$$

To figure the different ways of arranging n items if all n items are chosen one at a time, we could use the Fundamental Counting Rule. We then multiply the options of each item $n(n-1)(n-2)\cdots 1$ until the last one is chosen which is $n!$

Examples:

    a. In a small class of 10 students, there are 10 seats available and all seats will be taken. Find the number of ways of arranging these 10 students.

        Since the seats are taken one at a time, we reduce each possibility by one until we reach the last one.

        To figure the total number of ways of arranging these students we multiply 10(9)(8)(7)(6)(5)(4)(3)(2)(1) so the answer is 3,628,800. This means that we have 3,628,800 different ways of arranging these students. We can use the factorial symbol to represent the product of all integers from 10 to 1. We denote 10 factorial as $10! = 3,628,800$.

    b. In a science laboratory, the maximum number of students allowed is 12. Find the number of ways of arranging 12 students in the 12 lab seats.

        Since there are 12 seats available and all 12 will be used, the number of arrangements is 12!.

        $12! = 479,001,600$

Your Turn to Practice

Compute the following.

    1. 6!

    2. $(9 - 4)!$

    3. $\dfrac{120!}{119!}$

4. $13!$

5. $\dfrac{88!}{90!}$

6. $20!$

7. $\dfrac{n!}{(n+1)!}$

8. In a conference, the maximum number of people allowed is 8. Find the number of ways of arranging all 8 people that are chosen.

If we choose a subset r from a total of n available slots, we use the permutations and combinations formulas to compute the total number of possibilities. If order matters, we compute the total permutations (or arrangements). If order does not matter, we compute the total combinations.

$$_nP_r = \dfrac{n!}{(n-r)!}$$

$$_nC_r = \dfrac{n!}{r!(n-r)!}$$

Examples:

a. From a group of 10 students, 3 will be selected to attend a conference. How many ways can these 3 students be chosen?

Since order does not matter, we compute the combination of 10 choose 3.

$$_nC_r = \frac{10!}{3!(10-3)!}$$

$$= \frac{10!}{3!(7)!}$$

$$= \frac{10(9)(8)(7)(6)(5)(4)(3)(2)(1)}{3(2)(1)(7)(6)(5)(4)(3)(2)(1)}$$

$$= 120$$

b. From another group of 10 students, 3 will be selected to attend a conference. The first student chosen will lead the group, the second student will be the note taker, and the third student will oversee the travel plans. How many ways can these 3 students be chosen?

Since order *does* matter, we compute the permutation of 10 choose 3.

$$_nP_r = \frac{10!}{(10-3)!}$$

$$= \frac{10!}{(7)!}$$

$$= \frac{10(9)(8)(7)(6)(5)(4)(3)(2)(1)}{7(6)(5)(4)(3)(2)(1)}$$

$$= 720$$

Your Turn to Practice

1. In a lottery with 52 numbers available, to win the grand prize one needs to come up with the winning selection of 6 numbers. Find the total possible combinations that can be played.

2. From a list of 8 volunteers, 4 will be chosen to form a committee. How many different possible committees of 4 can be formed?

3. From another list of 7 volunteers, 4 will be chosen to form a committee. The first one chosen will be the committee chair, the second one will be the vice-chair, the third will be the secretary and the fourth will be the treasurer. How many different possible committees of 4 can be formed?

Chapter 5 Probability Distributions

5.1 Verify the Validity of a Probability Distribution

As we discussed in Chapter 4, probability values must lie within the values of 0 to 1 (or in percentage form within 0% to 100%). When working with probability distributions, we must always verify two conditions. First, the probability of each X, in other words $P(X)$, is any number within the range 0 to 1. The second rule is that the sum of all $P(X)$ values must equal 1. Discrete probability distributions are finite and countable where X is the value of each discrete outcome and $P(X)$ is the probability of each discrete outcome. These discrete probability distributions can be organized in a table with each possible X value listed in one row and the associated probability, $P(X)$ listed in another row. The example below shows this format.

Example:

Determine if the given distribution is a valid probability distribution or not. Explain your reasoning.

a.

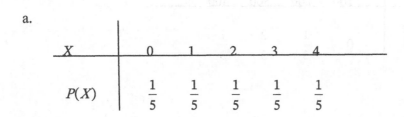

Yes, this is a valid probability distribution since the two conditions are satisfied.

i) $\sum P(X) = \dfrac{1}{5} + \dfrac{1}{5} + \dfrac{1}{5} + \dfrac{1}{5} + \dfrac{1}{5} = 1$

ii) Each $P(X)$ is between 0 and 1.

b.

X	5	6	7	8
$P(X)$	0.15	0.10	0.80	−0.05

No, this is not a valid probability distribution. $P(8)$ is negative which is not possible since $P(X)$ must be between 0 and 1. Note that the probabilities do sum to 1 $(0.15 + 0.10 + 0.80 − 0.05 = 1)$, but this is not sufficient because one of the probabilities is less than zero. BOTH conditions must hold for a probability distribution to be valid.

c.

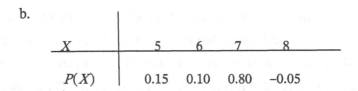

X	100	200	300	400
$P(X)$	0	$\dfrac{1}{3}$	$\dfrac{2}{3}$	$\dfrac{1}{3}$

No, this is not a probability distribution since $\sum P(X) = \dfrac{4}{3} \neq 1$.

In this case, each of the individual probabilities is between 0 and 1, but the sum is greater than 1. Again, BOTH must hold for a probability distribution to be valid.

116

d.

X	4	8	12	16
P(X)	0.02	0.04	0.01	0.03

No, this is not a probability distribution since $\sum P(X) = 0.10 < 1$

As with part (c), each of the individual probabilities is between 0 and 1, but the sum is less than 1. Again, BOTH must hold for a probability distribution to be valid.

e. $X = 1, 2, 3, 4 \qquad P(X) = \dfrac{X}{10}$

First, we find the value of each $P(X)$, by substituting each X value into the function. We can organize X and $P(X)$ in the form of a table. *Note: it is not necessary to reduce the fractions although it is customary.*

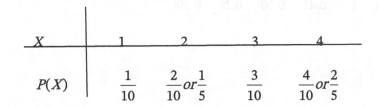

X	1	2	3	4
P(X)	$\dfrac{1}{10}$	$\dfrac{2}{10} or \dfrac{1}{5}$	$\dfrac{3}{10}$	$\dfrac{4}{10} or \dfrac{2}{5}$

Yes, this is a valid probability distribution since the two conditions are satisfied.

i) $\sum P(X) = \dfrac{1}{10} + \dfrac{2}{10} + \dfrac{3}{10} + \dfrac{4}{10} = 1$

ii) Each $P(X)$ is between 0 and 1.

Your Turn to Practice

Determine if the given distribution is a valid probability distribution or not. Explain your reasoning, making sure to check both conditions.

1.

X	8	9	10	11	12
P(X)	$\frac{1}{7}$	$\frac{1}{7}$	$\frac{2}{7}$	$\frac{1}{7}$	$\frac{1}{7}$

2.

X	97	98	99	100
P(X)	0.41	0.10	0.29	0.20

3.

X	50	60	70	80
P(X)	0	$\frac{1}{4}$	$\frac{1}{2}$	$\frac{3}{4}$

4. $X = 11, 12, 13 \qquad P(X) = \dfrac{X}{25}$

5.

X	5	10	15	20
$P(X)$	0.15	0.75	−0.2	0.3

5.2 Expected Values

The expected value of a discrete random variable is the theoretical average of the variable. In other words, the average value that is expected is that for the whole population, assuming the theoretical probabilities hold for the population. Given a discrete probability distribution, we compute the expected value as the sum of all $X \cdot P(X)$ values. The formula is then:

$$\mu = \sum X \cdot P(X)$$

Examples:

For the given discrete probability distribution, compute the expected value.

a. In a lottery, the winning is prize is $5000. If each ticket costs $10 and exactly 1000 tickets will be sold, find the expected value if someone buys one ticket.

Since there is only 1 possible way to win out of 1000, the probability of winning is $\frac{1}{1000}$ and the probability of losing is $\frac{999}{1000}$. Regardless of whether you win or lose, you must pay a cost of $10. The gain is a negative if you lose. In other words the gain is –$10. If you win, the gain is $5000 minus the $10 cost of the ticket, for a net gain of $4990. We can set up a probability distribution by letting X represent the net gain.

	Win	Lose
Net gain X	4990	–10
Probability $P(X)$	$\dfrac{1}{1000}$	$\dfrac{999}{1000}$

$$\mu = 4990 \cdot \frac{1}{1000} + (-10) \cdot \frac{999}{1000} = -5$$

This means that the average is a loss of $5 or an expected value of –$5. Note that 999 people who buy a ticket will lose $10 and one (lucky) person will win $4990. On average, a person buying a ticket expects to lose $5. Also, note that the expected net gain is not equal to an actual outcome of the lottery. It is okay for this to happen, because the expected net gain is what we expect to see *on average*.

b. In a different lottery, there are many prizes to win. One prize is $5000, another prize is $100, another one is $50, and then there are ten $5 gift certificates for a coffee shop. If each ticket costs $4 and exactly 2000 tickets will be sold, find the expected value if someone buys one ticket.

Since there are several possible ways to win out of 2000, there are various probability values of winning depending on the prize.

The probability of winning the $5000 prize is $\frac{1}{2000}$.

The probability of winning the $100 prize is $\frac{1}{2000}$.

The probability of winning the $50 prize is $\frac{1}{2000}$.

The probability of winning the $5 gift certificate prize is $\frac{10}{2000}$ since there are ten $5 gift certificates.

Altogether, there are 13 ways to win out of 2000, so the probability of losing is $\frac{1987}{2000}$. Regardless of whether you win or lose, you must pay a cost of $4. The gain is a negative if you lose—in other words –$4. For the winnings, the gains are:

$5000 minus the $4 = $4996, $100 minus the $4 = $96, $50 minus the $4 = $46, $5 minus the $4 = $1.

We can set up a discrete probability distribution by letting X represent the net gain.

	Win $5000	Win $100	Win $50	Win $5 gift certificate	Lose
Net gain X	4996	96	46	1	–4
Probability $P(X)$	$\dfrac{1}{2000}$	$\dfrac{1}{2000}$	$\dfrac{1}{2000}$	$\dfrac{10}{2000}$	$\dfrac{1987}{2000}$

$$\mu = 4996 \cdot \frac{1}{2000} + 96 \cdot \frac{1}{2000} + 46 \cdot \frac{1}{2000} + 1 \cdot \frac{10}{2000} + (-4) \cdot \frac{1987}{2000}$$

$$= 2.498 + 0.048 + 0.023 + 0.005 - 3.974$$

$$= -1.40$$

This means that the average is a loss of $1.40 or an expected value of –$1.40.

Your Turn to Practice

For the given situation, compute the expected value.

1. In a lottery, the winning is prize is $10,000. If each ticket costs $20 and exactly 500 tickets will be sold, find the expected net gain if someone buys one ticket.

122

2. In another raffle, there are many winning prizes. One prize is $1000, another prize is $200, and then there are eight $10 gift cards. If each ticket costs $3 and exactly 800 tickets will be sold, find the expected net gain if someone buys one ticket.

3. In the same lottery as in #2 above, we will modify the winnings so that a winning ticket gets to keep the $3 along with the winning prize. One prize is $1000, another prize is $200, and then there are eight $10 gift cards. If each ticket costs $3 and exactly 800 tickets will be sold, find the expected net gain if someone buys one ticket.

5.3 Binomial Distribution

In a binomial distribution, there are four conditions that must satisfied. As the word binomial implies, there are two possible outcomes, specifically success or failure. However, there are three other conditions that must be satisfied as well.

The four conditions for a binomial distribution are:

1. Two possible outcomes: Success or Failure.
2. Fixed number of trials: We use n to represent the total number of trials.
3. The events must be independent of each other.
4. The probability of success/failure must remain constant throughout the experiment. We let p represent the success rate of each trial and q represent the failure rate of each trial.

Examples:

Determine if the given experiment can be classified as a binomial experiment. If not, state why not.

a. A True/False exam that consists of 60 questions.

Condition #1 is satisfied. A question is either correct or incorrect. We can assign the success to be answering correctly, so a failure is answering incorrectly. Alternatively, we can assign answering incorrectly as the success of the experiment, thus assigning failure for a correct answer. In either scenario, there are only two possible outcomes.

Condition #2 is satisfied. The total number of trials is 60, because it is a 60-question exam. $n = 60$

<u>Condition #3 is satisfied</u>. In a True/False exam, the answer to one question does not depend on the answer to another question. Thus, the answer to each problem is assumed to be independent of the others, so each trial is independent.

<u>Condition #4 is satisfied</u>. Assuming success is answering a true/false question correctly, the success rate of each question, $p = \dfrac{1}{2} = 0.5$ remains the same throughout the entire test. Consequently, the failure rate of each question, $q = \dfrac{1}{2} = 0.5$ also remains the same throughout the entire test. Since the four conditions are satisfied, the 60-question true/false exam is a binomial experiment.

b. A multiple-choice exam that consists of 60 questions with possible answers a, b, c, d, or e.

<u>Condition #1 is satisfied</u>. A multiple-choice question is either correct or incorrect. There are five options for each question, but only one is correct and the other four are incorrect. We can assign the success to be answering correctly, so a failure is answering incorrectly. There are only two possible outcomes.

<u>Condition #2 is satisfied</u>. The total number of trials is 60, because it is a 60-question exam. $n = 60$

<u>Condition #3 is satisfied</u>. In a multiple-choice exam, the answer to one question does not depend on the answer to another question. The answer to each problem is assumed to be independent of the others, so each trial is independent.

<u>Condition #4</u> is satisfied. Assuming that a success is choosing the correct option in a multiple-choice question with five options available, the success rate of each question, $p = \dfrac{1}{5} = 0.2$ remains the same throughout the entire exam. Consequently, the failure rate of each question, $q = \dfrac{4}{5} = 0.8$ also remains the same throughout the entire exam. Since the four conditions are satisfied, the 60-question multiple-choice exam with possible answers *a, b, c, d, and e* is a binomial experiment.

In the last example, it was important to note that condition # 1 requiring only two possible outcomes namely success or failure was still satisfied. The answer chosen would be either correct or incorrect regardless of the number of available options.

Your Turn to Practice

Determine if the given experiment can be classified as a binomial experiment. If not, state why not.

1. A multiple-choice exam that consists of 60 questions with five possible answers (*a, b, c, d, e*) on the first 40 questions and four possible answers (*a, b, c, d*) on the last 20 questions.

126

2. An algebra test with 20 questions. The professor gives partial credit if most of the work is correct.

3. A student did not prepare for an entrance exam consisting of 100 questions that are all multiple choice with six choices (*a, b, c, d, e, f*) provided in each question.

4. In a business class, the professor gives an essay exam to discuss the benefits of financial planning. Partial credit is available.

Once an experiment is classified as binomial, we can then use a formula to compute the probability of a given number of X successes in n trials. Since n is the total, then X is an integer from 0 to n, so $X = 0$ means there are no successes and $X = n$ means all are successes. This is called the binomial probability and the formula is

$$P(X) = \frac{n!}{(n-X)!X!} p^X q^{n-X} \quad , X = 0, 1, 2, ..., n$$

Since $\dfrac{n!}{(n-x)!x!}$ is the same as $_nC_X$ we can also express the binomial probability formula as

$$P(X) = {_nC_X} p^X q^{n-X} \quad , X = 0, 1, 2, ..., n$$

Examples:

Given the values of X, n, and p, compute the probability of X successes using the binomial probability formula.

a. $n = 5, \quad p = 0.30, \quad X = 4$

$$P(4) = \frac{5!}{(5-4)!4!} (0.30)^4 (0.70)^{5-4} \quad \text{or} \quad P(4) = {_5C_4} (0.30)^4 (0.70)^{5-4}$$

$$P(4) = 5(0.30)^4 (0.70)^1$$

$$P(4) \approx 0.028$$

b. $n = 6, \quad p = 0.44, \quad X = 2$

$$P(2) = \frac{6!}{(6-2)!2!} (0.44)^2 (0.56)^{6-2} \quad \text{or} \quad P(2) = {_6C_2} (0.44)^2 (0.56)^{6-2}$$

$$P(2) = 15(0.44)^2 (0.56)^4$$

$$P(2) \approx 0.286$$

128

When finding the binomial probability, we can always use either form of the formula or we have the option of a table of binomial probability values. The values found on this table were computed using the formula and organized in an easy to read list.

Since X can take on any integer value from 0 to n, we need to be careful of binomial probabilities that use the words: exactly, greater than or more than, less than or fewer than, at least, at most, does not exceed or no more than.

- Probability of **Exactly** X number of successes: $P(X = \text{number})$
- Probability of **at least** X number of successes: $P(X \geq \text{number}) = P(X = \text{number or more})$
- Probability of **more than** X number of successes: $P(X > \text{number}) = P(X \text{ is greater but not equal to the number})$
- Probability of **at most** X number of successes: $P(X \leq \text{number}) = P(X = \text{number or less})$
- Probability of **less than** X number of successes: $P(X < \text{number}) = P(X \text{ is less than but not equal to the number})$

Other phrases such as **does not exceed** or **no more than** can used in place of at most.

Examples:

Given the values of X, n, and p, compute the probability of X successes using the binomial distribution table.

a. $n = 5$, $p = 0.30$, X is exactly 4

p

n	X	0.05	...	0.3
5	0			0.168
	1			0.360
	2			0.309
	3			0.132
	4			0.077
	5			0.010

From the table, we obtain P(4) = 0.077

129

b. $n = 5$, $p = 0.30$, X is at least 3

At least 3 means 3 or more, so $X = 3, 4,$ or 5

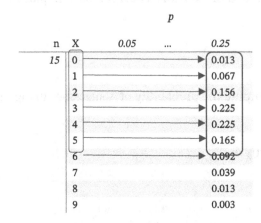

			p	
n	X	0.05	...	0.3
5	0			0.168
	1			0.360
	2			0.309
	3			0.132
	4			0.077
	5			0.010

From the table, we obtain $P(3) + P(4) + P(5) = 0.132 + 0.077 + 0.010$

$$= 0.219$$

c. $n = 15$, $p = 0.25$, X is at most 6

At most 6 means 6 or less, so $X = 0, 1, 2, 3, 4, 5$ or 6

			p	
n	X	0.05	...	0.25
15	0			0.013
	1			0.067
	2			0.156
	3			0.225
	4			0.225
	5			0.165
	6			0.092
	7			0.039
	8			0.013
	9			0.003

From the table, we obtain $P(0) + P(1) + P(2) + P(3) + P(4) + P(5) + P(6)$

$$= 0.013 + 0.067 + 0.156 + 0.225 + 0.225 + 0.165 + 0.092$$

$$= 0.943$$

130

d. $n = 8$, $p = 0.60$, X is less than 2

Less than 2 means below 2, so $X = 0$ or 1

			p	
n	X	0.05	...	0.6
8	0			0.001
	1			0.008
	2			0.041
	3			0.124
	4			0.232
	5			0.279

From the table, we obtain $P(0) + P(1) = 0.001 + 0.008$

$$= 0.009$$

e. $n = 8$, $p = 0.60$, X is 0

			p	
n	X	0.05	...	0.6
8	0			0.001
	1			0.008
	2			0.041
	3			0.124
	4			0.232
	5			0.279

From the table, we obtain $P(0) = 0.001$

Your Turn to Practice

For questions 1 – 5 use the following information. A student will be taking a quiz he is underprepared for and will guess every answer. The quiz consists of 10 true/false questions. Find the probability that he guesses:

1. Exactly 7 questions correctly.   [*Use both the Binomial Distribution table and the formula to compute the answer in this case.*]

2. All questions correctly.

3. At least 7 questions correctly

4. No questions correctly

5. At most 7 questions correctly

For questions 6 – 8 use the following information. Another student will be taking a multiple-choice exam she is underprepared for and will guess every answer. The exam consists of 20 multiple-choice questions with five possible answers (*a, b, c, d, e*). Find the probability that she guesses:

6. No questions correctly.

7. All questions correctly.

8. Less than 10 questions correctly.

Chapter 6 Normal Distribution

6.1 Apply the Inequalities $<, >, \leq, \geq$ to Find Probabilities for Normal Distributions

In Section 1.2, we reviewed the inequality symbols and their use when comparing numbers. In algebra when we solve linear inequalities, we graph the solution of that inequality on a number line. If the number we are comparing to is included, we include the endpoint (visually a solid circle); if the number we are comparing to is not included, we exclude the endpoint (visually an open circle).

Examples:

Graph the following linear inequalities.

a. $X > 4$

This inequality means that we want values where the variable X is strictly greater than 4, so we have an open circle at 4 and a solid line to the right.

134

b. $X \geq 4$

This inequality means that we want values where the variable X is greater than or equal to 4, so we have a closed circle at 4 and a solid line to the right. The difference between this example and the previous example is that here the value $X = 4$ is included.

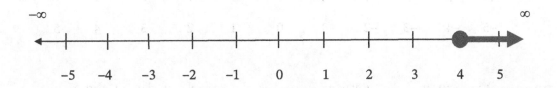

c. $X < 4$

This inequality means that we want values where the variable X is strictly less than 4, so we have an open circle at 4 and a solid line to the left.

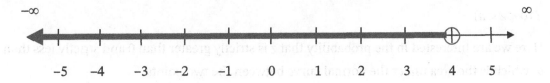

d. $X \leq 4$

This inequality means that we want values where the variable X is less than or equal to 4, so we have a closed circle at 4 and a solid line to the left. The difference between this example and the previous example is that here the value $X = 4$ is included.

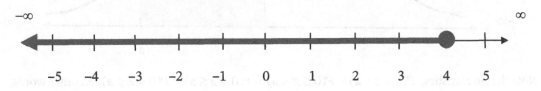

e. $1 \leq X < 4$

135

This inequality means that we want values where the variable X is greater than or equal to 1 AND strictly less than 4, so we have a closed circle at 1 (to show that $X = 1$ is included) and a solid line to the right, ending with an open circle at $X = 4$ to show that this value is excluded.

When working with the normal distribution, we draw a number line that is infinite in both directions and draw the normal curve above it. The inequalities will be used to identify the area under the curve, which is the same as probability. The z values or z scores are plotted along the x-axis. Based on the inequality we are given, we shade the corresponding area under the curve (representing the probability) to the left or right of the z value.

$P(0 < z < a)$

Here we are interested in the probability that z is strictly greater than 0 and strictly less than a, which is the area under the normal curve between the two points.

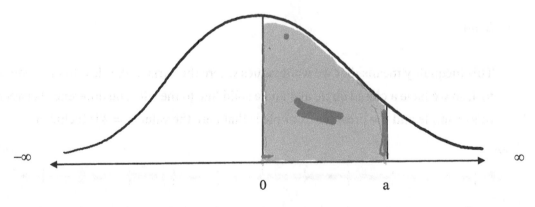

Note that in statistics, $P(0 < z < a) = P(0 \leq z < a) = P(0 \leq z \leq a) = P(0 < z \leq a)$. In other words, the probability or area between 0 and a is the same whether the endpoints are included or not. This

136

occurs, since this is a continuous distribution whereby the area at the endpoint is a vertical which a zero area value or a zero probability value.

Examples:

Draw the normal distribution and shade the appropriate area.

a. $P(0 < z < 3.00)$

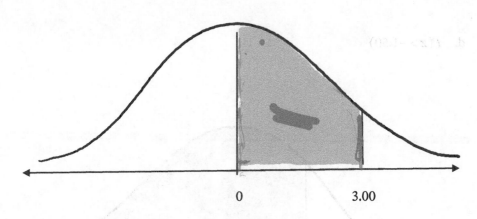

0   3.00

b. $P(z < 3.00)$

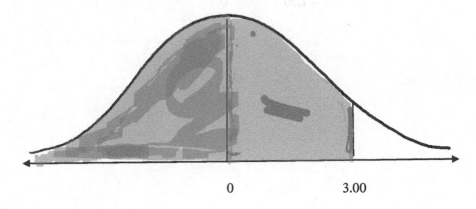

0   3.00

c. $P(z > 1.96)$

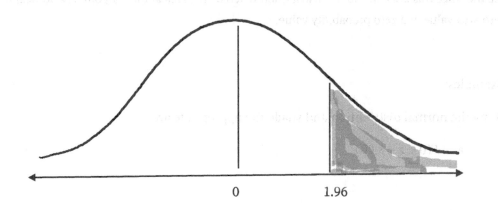

d. $P(z > -1.50)$

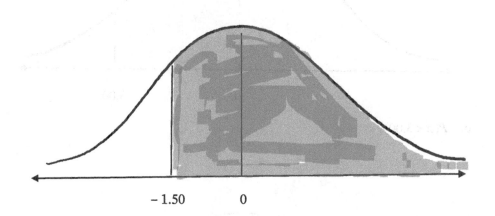

Your Turn to Practice

Draw the normal distribution and shade the appropriate area.

1. $P(z < 2.00)$

2. $P(z > -2.15)$

3. $P(0 < z < 1.23)$

4. $P(z < -3.04)$

5. $P(-2.25 < z < 1.50)$

6. $P(z > 1.00)$

6.2 Read and Interpret the z table

We have discussed using the Empirical Rule to find the percentage of scores within one, two, or three standard deviations from the mean for a normal distribution. Those percentages also represented the probabilities or areas under the normal curve within one, two, and three standard deviations of the mean, respectively. We can also use the Standard Normal Distribution table (also known as the z table) to find the area under the curve for other z values besides ±3, ±2, ±1 which we use for the Empirical Rule. The areas listed in the table are cumulative areas under the curve to the left of the given z value. In other words, the area that we get from the table is always the area under the curve to the left of that specific z value.

The procedure for finding the areas to the left of the given z value in the Standard Normal Distribution table (Table E) is as follows:

i.   Start with the first column on the left under z. All the values listed in that column are the z values with one decimal place.
ii.   The next columns .00 to .09 represent the second decimal place of the z value. The next step is to cross reference the row from that first column with the column containing the second decimal place.
iii. The number with 4 decimal places represents the cumulative area to the left of that z value.

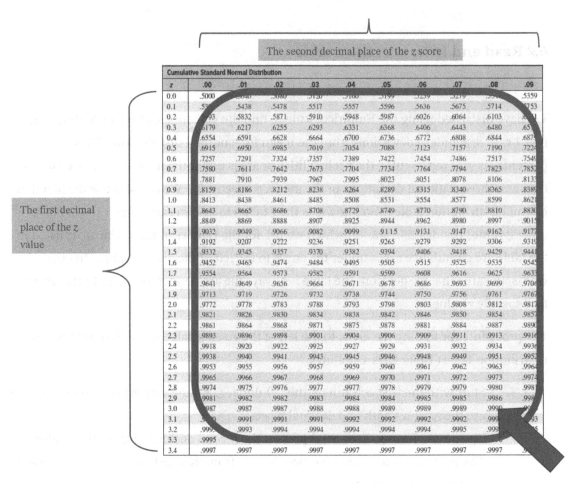

Cumulative Standard Normal Distribution

z	.00	.01	.02	.03	.04	.05	.06	.07	.08	.09
0.0	.5000	.5040	.5080	.5120	.5160	.5199	.5239	.5279	.5319	.5359
0.1	.5398	.5438	.5478	.5517	.5557	.5596	.5636	.5675	.5714	.5753
0.2	.5793	.5832	.5871	.5910	.5948	.5987	.6026	.6064	.6103	.6141
0.3	.6179	.6217	.6255	.6293	.6331	.6368	.6406	.6443	.6480	.6517
0.4	.6554	.6591	.6628	.6664	.6700	.6736	.6772	.6808	.6844	.6879
0.5	.6915	.6950	.6985	.7019	.7054	.7088	.7123	.7157	.7190	.7224
0.6	.7257	.7291	.7324	.7357	.7389	.7422	.7454	.7486	.7517	.7549
0.7	.7580	.7611	.7642	.7673	.7704	.7734	.7764	.7794	.7823	.7852
0.8	.7881	.7910	.7939	.7967	.7995	.8023	.8051	.8078	.8106	.8133
0.9	.8159	.8186	.8212	.8238	.8264	.8289	.8315	.8340	.8365	.8389
1.0	.8413	.8438	.8461	.8485	.8508	.8531	.8554	.8577	.8599	.8621
1.1	.8643	.8665	.8686	.8708	.8729	.8749	.8770	.8790	.8810	.8830
1.2	.8849	.8869	.8888	.8907	.8925	.8944	.8962	.8980	.8997	.9015
1.3	.9032	.9049	.9066	.9082	.9099	.9115	.9131	.9147	.9162	.9177
1.4	.9192	.9207	.9222	.9236	.9251	.9265	.9279	.9292	.9306	.9319
1.5	.9332	.9345	.9357	.9370	.9382	.9394	.9406	.9418	.9429	.9441
1.6	.9452	.9463	.9474	.9484	.9495	.9505	.9515	.9525	.9535	.9545
1.7	.9554	.9564	.9573	.9582	.9591	.9599	.9608	.9616	.9625	.9633
1.8	.9641	.9649	.9656	.9664	.9671	.9678	.9686	.9693	.9699	.9706
1.9	.9713	.9719	.9726	.9732	.9738	.9744	.9750	.9756	.9761	.9767
2.0	.9772	.9778	.9783	.9788	.9793	.9798	.9803	.9808	.9812	.9817
2.1	.9821	.9826	.9830	.9834	.9838	.9842	.9846	.9850	.9854	.9857
2.2	.9861	.9864	.9868	.9871	.9875	.9878	.9881	.9884	.9887	.9890
2.3	.9893	.9896	.9898	.9901	.9904	.9906	.9909	.9911	.9913	.9916
2.4	.9918	.9920	.9922	.9925	.9927	.9929	.9931	.9932	.9934	.9936
2.5	.9938	.9940	.9941	.9943	.9945	.9946	.9948	.9949	.9951	.9952
2.6	.9953	.9955	.9956	.9957	.9959	.9960	.9961	.9962	.9963	.9964
2.7	.9965	.9966	.9967	.9968	.9969	.9970	.9971	.9972	.9973	.9974
2.8	.9974	.9975	.9976	.9977	.9977	.9978	.9979	.9979	.9980	.9981
2.9	.9981	.9982	.9982	.9983	.9984	.9984	.9985	.9985	.9986	.9986
3.0	.9987	.9987	.9987	.9988	.9988	.9989	.9989	.9989	.9990	.9990
3.1	.9990	.9991	.9991	.9991	.9992	.9992	.9992	.9992	.9993	.9993
3.2	.9993	.9993	.9994	.9994	.9994	.9994	.9994	.9995	.9995	.9995
3.3	.9995									
3.4	.9997	.9997	.9997	.9997	.9997	.9997	.9997	.9997	.9997	.9998

The second decimal place of the z score

The first decimal place of the z value

AREA to the left of the z value

Example:

From the examples in Section 6.1, find the probability of each using the standard normal distribution.

a. $P(0 < z < 3.00)$

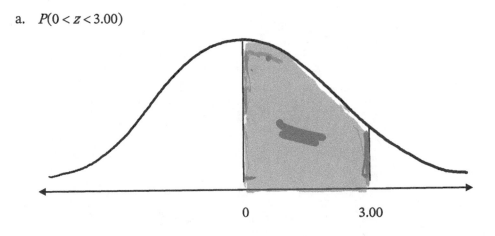

0   3.00

142

Cumulative Standard Normal Distribution

z	.00	.01	.02	.03	.04	.05	.06	.07	.08	.09
0.0	.5000	.5040	.5080	.5120	.5160	.5199	.5239	.5279	.5319	.5359
0.1	.5398	.5438	.5478	.5517	.5557	.5596	.5636	.5675	.5714	.5753
0.2	.5793	.5832	.5871	.5910	.5948	.5987	.6026	.6064	.6103	.6141
0.3	.6179	.6217	.6255	.6293	.6331	.6368	.6406	.6443	.6480	.6517
0.4	.6554	.6591	.6628	.6664	.6700	.6736	.6772	.6808	.6844	.6879
0.5	.6915	.6950	.6985	.7019	.7054	.7088	.7123	.7157	.7190	.7224
0.6	.7257	.7291	.7324	.7357	.7389	.7422	.7454	.7486	.7517	.7549
0.7	.7580	.7611	.7642	.7673	.7704	.7734	.7764	.7794	.7823	.7852
0.8	.7881	.7910	.7939	.7967	.7995	.8023	.8051	.8078	.8106	.8133
0.9	.8159	.8186	.8212	.8238	.8264	.8289	.8315	.8340	.8365	.8389
1.0	.8413	.8438	.8461	.8485	.8508	.8531	.8554	.8577	.8599	.8621
1.1	.8643	.8665	.8686	.8708	.8729	.8749	.8770	.8790	.8810	.8830
1.2	.8849	.8869	.8888	.8907	.8925	.8944	.8962	.8980	.8997	.9015
1.3	.9032	.9049	.9066	.9082	.9099	.9115	.9131	.9147	.9162	.9177
1.4	.9192	.9207	.9222	.9236	.9251	.9265	.9279	.9292	.9306	.9319
1.5	.9332	.9345	.9357	.9370	.9382	.9394	.9406	.9418	.9429	.9441
1.6	.9452	.9463	.9474	.9484	.9495	.9505	.9515	.9525	.9535	.9545
1.7	.9554	.9564	.9573	.9582	.9591	.9599	.9608	.9616	.9625	.9633
1.8	.9641	.9649	.9656	.9664	.9671	.9678	.9686	.9693	.9699	.9706
1.9	.9713	.9719	.9726	.9732	.9738	.9744	.9750	.9756	.9761	.9767
2.0	.9772	.9778	.9783	.9788	.9793	.9798	.9803	.9808	.9812	.9817
2.1	.9821	.9826	.9830	.9834	.9838	.9842	.9846	.9850	.9854	.9857
2.2	.9861	.9864	.9868	.9871	.9875	.9878	.9881	.9884	.9887	.9890
2.3	.9893	.9896	.9898	.9901	.9904	.9906	.9909	.9911	.9913	.9916
2.4	.9918	.9920	.9922	.9925	.9927	.9929	.9931	.9932	.9934	.9936
2.5	.9938	.9940	.9941	.9943	.9945	.9946	.9948	.9949	.9951	.9952
2.6	.9953	.9955	.9956	.9957	.9959	.9960	.9961	.9962	.9963	.9964
2.7	.9965	.9966	.9967	.9968	.9969	.9970	.9971	.9972	.9973	.9974
2.8	.9974	.9975	.9976	.9977	.9977	.9978	.9979	.9979	.9980	.9981
2.9	.9981	.9982	.9982	.9983	.9984	.9984	.9985	.9985	.9986	.9986
3.0	.9987	.9987	.9987	.9988	.9988	.9989	.9989	.9989	.9990	.9990
3.1	.9990	.9991	.9991	.9991	.9992	.9992	.9992	.9992	.9993	.9993
3.2	.9993	.9993	.9994	.9994	.9994	.9994	.9994	.9995	.9995	.9995
3.3	.9995	.9995	.9995	.9996	.9996	.9996	.9996	.9996	.9996	.9997
3.4	.9997	.9997	.9997	.9997	.9997	.9997	.9997	.9997	.9997	.9998

From the Standard Normal Distribution table, we find that the area to the left of $z = 3.00$ is 0.9987. Since we are looking for the area between $z = 0$ and $z = 3.00$, we subtract out the area to left of $z = 0$ which is 0.5000 (or 0.5) from 0.9987. We get $0.9987 - 0.5000 = 0.4987$ or 49.87%

b. $P(z < 3.00)$

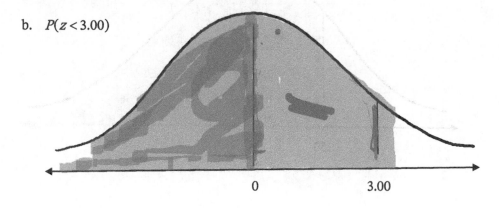

143

From the table, we find that the area to the left of $z = 3.00$ is 0.9987 or 99.87%. Note that this probability is 0.50 more than the probability of the previous example, because here we include the probability for z scores less than 0.

c. $P(z > 1.96)$

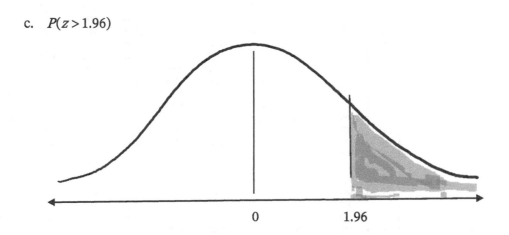

0   1.96

From the table, we find that the area to the left of $z = 1.96$ is 0.9750. Since we are looking for the area to the right of $z = 1.96$, we subtract the area to left of $z = 1.96$ which is 0.9750 from 1.000 (or 1). We get $1.000 - 0.9750 = 0.0250$ or 2.50%

d. $P(z > -1.50)$

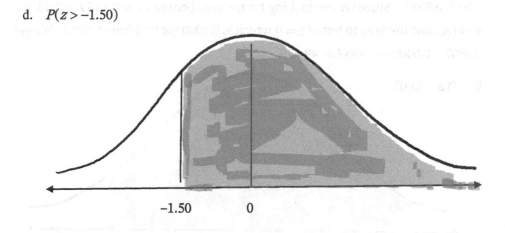

−1.50   0

From the table, we find that the area to the left of $z = -1.50$ is 0.0668. Since we are looking for the area to the right of $z = -1.50$, we subtract the area to left of $z = -1.50$ which is 0.0668 from 1.000 (or 1). We get $1.000 - 0.0668 = 0.9332$ or 93.32%

Your Turn to Practice

Find the probability for each using the standard normal distribution.

1. $P(z < 2.00)$

2. $P(z > -2.15)$

3. $P(0 < z < 1.23)$

4. $P(z < -3.04)$

5. $P(-2.25 < z < 1.50)$

6. $P(z > 1.00)$

The procedure for finding the z value(s) that corresponds to the given area is as follows:

i. Start with the cumulative area to the left of the z value. If the area to the right is given, then subtract that area from 1.000. If the area given is between 0 and the z value, then add 0.5000 to obtain the cumulative area to the left of that z value. We must do this, because the Standard Normal Distribution table will <u>only</u> list the cumulative area to the left of the z value.

ii. Refer to the area section in the Standard Normal Distribution table and locate the given area. If the exact area is not on the table, use the closest area value to it.

iii. The number with 4 decimal places represents the cumulative area to the left of that z value. After the cumulative area or probability to the left is found, we identify the corresponding z score by cross-referencing the row for the first decimal place with the column representing the second decimal place of that z score.

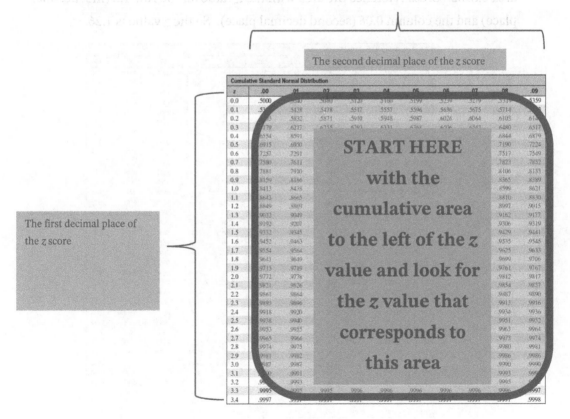

Examples:

Finding the z value that corresponds to the given area.

a.

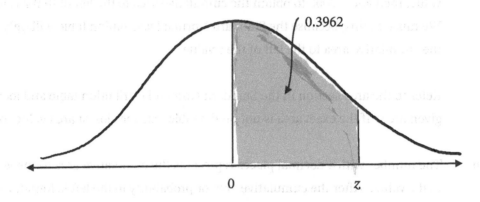

0.3962

0   z

Since the given area is between 0 and the z value, then add 0.5000 to 0.3962 cumulative area to the left of that z value. $0.5000 + 0.3962 = 0.8962$. Lookup the area 0.8962. Cross-reference the area with the z value on the row 1.2 (first decimal place) and the column 0.06 (second decimal place). So the z value is 1.26.

Cumulative Standard Normal Distribution

z	.00	.01	.02	.03	.04	.05	.06	.07	.08	.09
0.0	.5000	.5040	.5080	.5120	.5160	.5199	.5239	.5279	.5319	.5359
0.1	.5398	.5438	.5478	.5517	.5557	.5596	.5636	.5675	.5714	.5753
0.2	.5793	.5832	.5871	.5910	.5948	.5987	.6026	.6064	.6103	.6141
0.3	.6179	.6217	.6255	.6293	.6331	.6368	.6406	.6443	.6480	.6517
0.4	.6554	.6591	.6628	.6664	.6700	.6736	.6772	.6808	.6844	.6879
0.5	.6915	.6950	.6985	.7019	.7054	.7088	.7123	.7157	.7190	.7224
0.6	.7257	.7291	.7324	.7357	.7389	.7422	.7454	.7486	.7517	.7549
0.7	.7580	.7611	.7642	.7673	.7704	.7734	.7764	.7794	.7823	.7852
0.8	.7881	.7910	.7939	.7967	.7995	.8023	.8051	.8078	.8106	.8133
0.9	.8159	.8186	.8212	.8238	.8264	.8289	.8315	.8340	.8365	.8389
1.0	.8413	.8438	.8461	.8485	.8508	.8531	.8554	.8577	.8599	.8621
1.1	.8643	.8665	.8686	.8708	.8729	.8749	.8770	.8790	.8810	.8830
1.2	.8849	.8869	.8888	.8907	.8925	.8944	.8962	.8980	.8997	.9015
1.3	.9032	.9049	.9066	.9082	.9099	.9115	.9131	.9147	.9162	.9177
1.4	.9192	.9207	.9222	.9236	.9251	.9265	.9279	.9292	.9306	.9319
1.5	.9332	.9345	.9357	.9370	.9382	.9394	.9406	.9418	.9429	.9441
1.6	.9452	.9463	.9474	.9484	.9495	.9505	.9515	.9525	.9535	.9545
1.7	.9554	.9564	.9573	.9582	.9591	.9599	.9608	.9616	.9625	.9633
1.8	.9641	.9649	.9656	.9664	.9671	.9678	.9686	.9693	.9699	.9706
1.9	.9713	.9719	.9726	.9732	.9738	.9744	.9750	.9756	.9761	.9767
2.0	.9772	.9778	.9783	.9788	.9793	.9798	.9803	.9808	.9812	.9817
2.1	.9821	.9826	.9830	.9834	.9838	.9842	.9846	.9850	.9854	.9857
2.2	.9861	.9864	.9868	.9871	.9875	.9878	.9881	.9884	.9887	.9890
2.3	.9893	.9896	.9898	.9901	.9904	.9906	.9909	.9911	.9913	.9916
2.4	.9918	.9920	.9922	.9925	.9927	.9929	.9931	.9932	.9934	.9936
2.5	.9938	.9940	.9941	.9943	.9945	.9946	.9948	.9949	.9951	.9952
2.6	.9953	.9955	.9956	.9957	.9959	.9960	.9961	.9962	.9963	.9964
2.7	.9965	.9966	.9967	.9968	.9969	.9970	.9971	.9972	.9973	.9974
2.8	.9974	.9975	.9976	.9977	.9977	.9978	.9979	.9979	.9980	.9981
2.9	.9981	.9982	.9982	.9983	.9984	.9984	.9985	.9985	.9986	.9986
3.0	.9987	.9987	.9987	.9988	.9988	.9989	.9989	.9989	.9990	.9990
3.1	.9990	.9991	.9991	.9991	.9992	.9992	.9992	.9992	.9993	.9993
3.2	.9993	.9993	.9994	.9994	.9994	.9994	.9994	.9995	.9995	.9995
3.3	.9995	.9995	.9995	.9996	.9996	.9996	.9996	.9996	.9996	.9997
3.4	.9997	.9997	.9997	.9997	.9997	.9997	.9997	.9997	.9997	.9998

148

b.

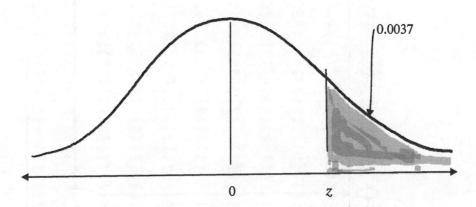

Since the given area is to the right of the z value, then subtract that area from 1.000 to obtain the cumulative area to the left of that z value. $1.000 - 0.0037 = 0.9963$. Lookup the area 0.9963. Cross reference the area with the z value on the row 2.6 (first decimal place) and the column 0.08 (second decimal place). So the z value is 2.68.

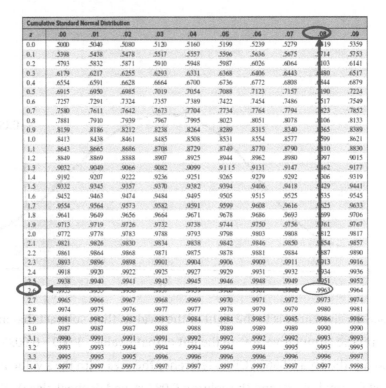

z	.00	.01	.02	.03	.04	.05	.06	.07	.08	.09
0.0	.5000	.5040	.5080	.5120	.5160	.5199	.5239	.5279	.5319	.5359
0.1	.5398	.5438	.5478	.5517	.5557	.5596	.5636	.5675	.5714	.5753
0.2	.5793	.5832	.5871	.5910	.5948	.5987	.6026	.6064	.6103	.6141
0.3	.6179	.6217	.6255	.6293	.6331	.6368	.6406	.6443	.6480	.6517
0.4	.6554	.6591	.6628	.6664	.6700	.6736	.6772	.6808	.6844	.6879
0.5	.6915	.6950	.6985	.7019	.7054	.7088	.7123	.7157	.7190	.7224
0.6	.7257	.7291	.7324	.7357	.7389	.7422	.7454	.7486	.7517	.7549
0.7	.7580	.7611	.7642	.7673	.7704	.7734	.7764	.7794	.7823	.7852
0.8	.7881	.7910	.7939	.7967	.7995	.8023	.8051	.8078	.8106	.8133
0.9	.8159	.8186	.8212	.8238	.8264	.8289	.8315	.8340	.8365	.8389
1.0	.8413	.8438	.8461	.8485	.8508	.8531	.8554	.8577	.8599	.8621
1.1	.8643	.8665	.8686	.8708	.8729	.8749	.8770	.8790	.8810	.8830
1.2	.8849	.8869	.8888	.8907	.8925	.8944	.8962	.8980	.8997	.9015
1.3	.9032	.9049	.9066	.9082	.9099	.9115	.9131	.9147	.9162	.9177
1.4	.9192	.9207	.9222	.9236	.9251	.9265	.9279	.9292	.9306	.9319
1.5	.9332	.9345	.9357	.9370	.9382	.9394	.9406	.9418	.9429	.9441
1.6	.9452	.9463	.9474	.9484	.9495	.9505	.9515	.9525	.9535	.9545
1.7	.9554	.9564	.9573	.9582	.9591	.9599	.9608	.9616	.9625	.9633
1.8	.9641	.9649	.9656	.9664	.9671	.9678	.9686	.9693	.9699	.9706
1.9	.9713	.9719	.9726	.9732	.9738	.9744	.9750	.9756	.9761	.9767
2.0	.9772	.9778	.9783	.9788	.9793	.9798	.9803	.9808	.9812	.9817
2.1	.9821	.9826	.9830	.9834	.9838	.9842	.9846	.9850	.9854	.9857
2.2	.9861	.9864	.9868	.9871	.9875	.9878	.9881	.9884	.9887	.9890
2.3	.9893	.9896	.9898	.9901	.9904	.9906	.9909	.9911	.9913	.9916
2.4	.9918	.9920	.9922	.9925	.9927	.9929	.9931	.9932	.9934	.9936
2.5	.9938	.9940	.9941	.9943	.9945	.9946	.9948	.9949	.9951	.9952
2.6									.9963	.9964
2.7	.9965	.9966	.9967	.9968	.9969	.9970	.9971	.9972	.9973	.9974
2.8	.9974	.9975	.9976	.9977	.9977	.9978	.9979	.9979	.9980	.9981
2.9	.9981	.9982	.9982	.9983	.9984	.9984	.9985	.9985	.9986	.9986
3.0	.9987	.9987	.9987	.9988	.9988	.9989	.9989	.9989	.9990	.9990
3.1	.9990	.9991	.9991	.9991	.9992	.9992	.9992	.9992	.9993	.9993
3.2	.9993	.9993	.9994	.9994	.9994	.9994	.9994	.9995	.9995	.9995
3.3	.9995	.9995	.9995	.9996	.9996	.9996	.9996	.9996	.9996	.9997
3.4	.9997	.9997	.9997	.9997	.9997	.9997	.9997	.9997	.9997	.9998

c. Find the z value that is to left of the mean such that 92.51% of the area lies to the right of it.

Since the z value is to left of the mean, it is negative in sign. Since the given area 0.9251 (or 92.51%) is to the right of the z value, then subtract that area from 1.000 to obtain the cumulative area to the left of that z value. $1.000 - 0.9251 = 0.0749$. Lookup the area 0.0749 for the negative z value. Cross reference the area with the z value on the row –1.4 (first decimal place) and the column 0.04 (second decimal place). So the z value is –1.44.

d. Find the z value that is to the right of the mean where 85.31% of the lies to the left of it.

150

Since the z value is to the right of the mean, it is positive in sign. Since the given area 0.8531 (or 85.31%) is to the left of the z value, we cross reference the area with the z value on the row 1.0 (first decimal place) and the column 0.05 (second decimal place). So the z value is 1.05.

e. Find the two z values (one is negative and the other positive) so that the middle 60% is bounded by the two values.

If we subtract 100% – 60%, we get a total of 40% for the two tail areas. Since the curve is symmetric with respect to the mean, we can divide the tail area by 2 giving us 20% at each tail. So the area to the left of the negative z value is 20% or 0.2000. We refer to the negative z values.

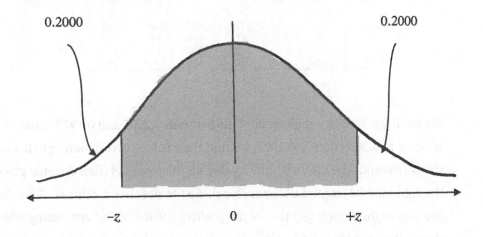

Cumulative Standard Normal Distribution

z	.00	.01	.02	.03	.04	.05	.06	.07	.08	.09
−3.4	.0003	.0003	.0003	.0003	.0003	.0003	.0003	.0003	.0003	.0002
−3.3	.0005	.0005	.0005	.0004	.0004	.0004	.0004	.0004	.0004	.0003
−3.2	.0007	.0007	.0006	.0006	.0006	.0006	.0006	.0005	.0005	.0005
−3.1	.0010	.0009	.0009	.0009	.0008	.0008	.0008	.0008	.0007	.0007
−3.0	.0013	.0013	.0013	.0012	.0012	.0011	.0011	.0011	.0010	.0010
−2.9	.0019	.0018	.0018	.0017	.0016	.0016	.0015	.0015	.0014	.0014
−2.8	.0026	.0025	.0024	.0023	.0023	.0022	.0021	.0021	.0020	.0019
−2.7	.0035	.0034	.0033	.0032	.0031	.0030	.0029	.0028	.0027	.0026
−2.6	.0047	.0045	.0044	.0043	.0041	.0040	.0039	.0038	.0037	.0036
−2.5	.0062	.0060	.0059	.0057	.0055	.0054	.0052	.0051	.0049	.0048
−2.4	.0082	.0080	.0078	.0075	.0073	.0071	.0069	.0068	.0066	.0064
−2.3	.0107	.0104	.0102	.0099	.0096	.0094	.0091	.0089	.0087	.0084
−2.2	.0139	.0136	.0132	.0129	.0125	.0122	.0119	.0116	.0113	.0110
−2.1	.0179	.0174	.0170	.0166	.0162	.0158	.0154	.0150	.0146	.0143
−2.0	.0228	.0222	.0217	.0212	.0207	.0202	.0197	.0192	.0188	.0183
−1.9	.0287	.0281	.0274	.0268	.0262	.0256	.0250	.0244	.0239	.0233
−1.8	.0359	.0351	.0344	.0336	.0329	.0322	.0314	.0307	.0301	.0294
−1.7	.0446	.0436	.0427	.0418	.0409	.0401	.0392	.0384	.0375	.0367
−1.6	.0548	.0537	.0526	.0516	.0505	.0495	.0485	.0475	.0465	.0455
−1.5	.0668	.0655	.0643	.0630	.0618	.0606	.0594	.0582	.0571	.0559
−1.4	.0808	.0793	.0778	.0764	.0749	.0735	.0721	.0708	.0694	.0681
−1.3	.0968	.0951	.0934	.0918	.0901	.0885	.0869	.0853	.0838	.0823
−1.2	.1151	.1131	.1112	.1093	.1075	.1056	.1038	.1020	.1003	.0985
−1.1	.1357	.1335	.1314	.1292	.1271	.1251	.1230	.1210	.1190	.1170
−1.0	.1587	.1562	.1539	.1515	.1492	.1469	.1446	.1423	.1401	.1379
−0.9	.1841	.1814	.1788	.1762	.1736	.1711	.1685	.1660	.1635	.1611
−0.8	.2119	.2090	.2061	.2033	.2005	.1977	.1949	.1922	.1894	.1867
−0.7	.2420	.2389	.2358	.2327	.2296	.2266	.2236	.2206	.2177	.2148
−0.6	.2743	.2709	.2676	.2643	.2611	.2578	.2546	.2514	.2483	.2451
−0.5	.3085	.3050	.3015	.2981	.2946	.2912	.2877	.2843	.2810	.2776
−0.4	.3446	.3409	.3372	.3336	.3300	.3264	.3228	.3192	.3156	.3121
−0.3	.3821	.3783	.3745	.3707	.3669	.3632	.3594	.3557	.3520	.3483
−0.2	.4207	.4168	.4129	.4090	.4052	.4013	.3974	.3936	.3897	.3859
−0.1	.4602	.4562	.4522	.4483	.4443	.4404	.4364	.4325	.4286	.4247
−0.0	.5000	.4960	.4920	.4880	.4840	.4801	.4761	.4721	.4681	.4641

We see the 0.2000 is not given but falls between 0.2005 and 0.1977. Since 0.2000 is closer to 0.2005 than is 0.1977, we find the z value corresponding to 0.2005. Cross reference the area with the z value on the row −0.8 (first decimal place) and the column 0.04 (second decimal place). So the negative z value is −0.84. Since the area to the right (right tail) of the positive z value is also 20%, using symmetry the positive z value is 0.84. Therefore, the two z values are ± 0.84.

f. Find the two z values (one is negative and the other positive) so that the total area of the two tails is 10%. Assume that we want an equal area in each tail.

Since the curve is symmetrical with respect to the mean, we can divide the total tail area by 2 giving us 5% at each tail. So the area to the left of the negative z value is 5% or 0.0500. We refer to the negative z values.

Cumulative Standard Normal Distribution									
z	.00	.01	.02	.03	.04	.05	.06	.07	.08	.09
−3.4	.0003	.0003	.0003	.0003	.0003	.0003	.0003	.0003	.0003	.0002
−3.3	.0005	.0005	.0005	.0004	.0004	.0004	.0004	.0004	.0004	.0003
−3.2	.0007	.0007	.0006	.0006	.0006	.0006	.0006	.0005	.0005	.0005
−3.1	.0010	.0009	.0009	.0009	.0008	.0008	.0008	.0008	.0007	.0007
−3.0	.0013	.0013	.0013	.0012	.0012	.0011	.0011	.0011	.0010	.0010
−2.9	.0019	.0018	.0018	.0017	.0016	.0016	.0015	.0015	.0014	.0014
−2.8	.0026	.0025	.0024	.0023	.0023	.0022	.0021	.0021	.0020	.0019
−2.7	.0035	.0034	.0033	.0032	.0031	.0030	.0029	.0028	.0027	.0026
−2.6	.0047	.0045	.0044	.0043	.0041	.0040	.0039	.0038	.0037	.0036
−2.5	.0062	.0060	.0059	.0057	.0055	.0054	.0052	.0051	.0049	.0048
−2.4	.0082	.0080	.0078	.0075	.0073	.0071	.0069	.0068	.0066	.0064
−2.3	.0107	.0104	.0102	.0099	.0096	.0094	.0091	.0089	.0087	.0084
−2.2	.0139	.0136	.0132	.0129	.0125	.0122	.0119	.0116	.0113	.0110
−2.1	.0179	.0174	.0170	.0166	.0162	.0158	.0154	.0150	.0146	.0143
−2.0	.0228	.0222	.0217	.0212	.0207	.0202	.0197	.0192	.0188	.0183
−1.9	.0287	.0281	.0274	.0268	.0262	.0256	.0250	.0244	.0239	.0233
−1.8	.0359	.0351	.0344	.0336	.0329	.0322	.0314	.0307	.0301	.0294
−1.7	.0446	.0436	.0427	.0418	.0409	.0401	.0392	.0384	.0375	.0367
−1.6	.0548	.0537	.0526	.0516	.0505	.0495	.0485	.0475	.0465	.0455
−1.5	.0668	.0655	.0643	.0630	.0618	.0606	.0594	.0582	.0571	.0559
−1.4	.0808	.0793	.0778	.0764	.0749	.0735	.0721	.0708	.0694	.0681
−1.3	.0968	.0951	.0934	.0918	.0901	.0885	.0869	.0853	.0838	.0823
−1.2	.1151	.1131	.1112	.1093	.1075	.1056	.1038	.1020	.1003	.0985
−1.1	.1357	.1335	.1314	.1292	.1271	.1251	.1230	.1210	.1190	.1170
−1.0	.1587	.1562	.1539	.1515	.1492	.1469	.1446	.1423	.1401	.1379
−0.9	.1841	.1814	.1788	.1762	.1736	.1711	.1685	.1660	.1635	.1611
−0.8	.2119	.2090	.2061	.2033	.2005	.1977	.1949	.1922	.1894	.1867
−0.7	.2420	.2389	.2358	.2327	.2296	.2266	.2236	.2206	.2177	.2148
−0.6	.2743	.2709	.2676	.2643	.2611	.2578	.2546	.2514	.2483	.2451
−0.5	.3085	.3050	.3015	.2981	.2946	.2912	.2877	.2843	.2810	.2776
−0.4	.3446	.3409	.3372	.3336	.3300	.3264	.3228	.3192	.3156	.3121
−0.3	.3821	.3783	.3745	.3707	.3669	.3632	.3594	.3557	.3520	.3483
−0.2	.4207	.4168	.4129	.4090	.4052	.4013	.3974	.3936	.3897	.3859
−0.1	.4602	.4562	.4522	.4483	.4443	.4404	.4364	.4325	.4286	.4247
−0.0	.5000	.4960	.4920	.4880	.4840	.4801	.4761	.4721	.4681	.4641

We see the 0.0500 is not given but falls between 0.0505 and 0.0495. Since it is exactly in the middle, we find the average of the two z values corresponding to 0.0500 and 0.0495. Cross reference the areas with the z values on the row −1.6 (first decimal place) and the columns 0.04 and 0.05 (second decimal place). The

153

average (or mean) of –1.64 and –1.65 equals –1.645. Rounding it off to two decimal places, the negative z value is –1.65. Since the area to the right (right tail) of the positive z value is also 5%, using symmetry the positive z value is 1.65. Therefore, the two z values are ± 1.65.

Your Turn to Practice

For Questions 1-3 find the z value that corresponds to the given area.

1.

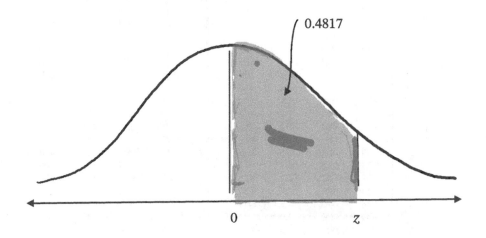

0.4817

2.

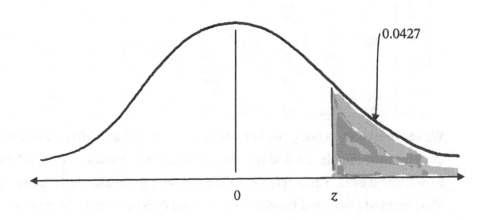

0.0427

3.

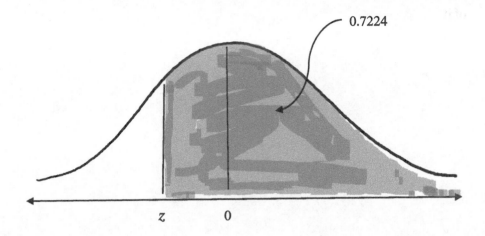

0.7224

z   0

4. Find the z value that is to the right of the mean such that 96.49% of the lies to the left of it.

5. Find the z value that is to the left of the mean such that 99.01% of the lies to the right of it.

6. Find the two z values (one is negative and the other positive) so that the total area of the two tails is 1%. Assume that we want an equal area in each tail.

7. Find the two z values (one is negative and the other positive) so that the middle 70% is bounded by the two values.

6.3 Finding Probabilities and Finding the Values of X for Specific Probabilities

In the previous section, we found the probability or area under the curve for the specified z value. We also found the z value for the corresponding given area. It is important to note the difference between the two procedures. In the first case, you are looking for the probability given a specified z value, whereas in the second case, you are given the probability and need to find the z value associated with it.

When working with any normal distribution that is not the standard normal distribution (with mean 0 and standard deviation 1), we must first convert X to z if we are trying to obtain the probability. On the other hand, if we are given the probability, we work backwards and find the z value first from the given probability and then solve for X.

157

The formula to convert X to z is

$$z = \frac{X - \mu}{\sigma}$$

If we want to find X, we could substitute all of the other values first and then algebraically solve for X. A quicker method is to use a modified version of the formula with X already solved in terms of the other variables as follows:

$$X = z\sigma + \mu$$

Examples:

In a major city that is highly populated, most people commute to work by driving. In a study, it was determined that the mean travel time in the morning during peak traffic from their homes to their jobs is 45 minutes with a standard deviation of 5.2 minutes. Assume the travel time is normally distributed. Find each of the following.

a. If a person driving to work is randomly selected, find the probability that the person takes more than 55 minutes to get to work.

We draw the normal curve. In this question, we are finding the probability so we must convert the X value to z. Then refer to the z table to find the cumulative area to the left of the z value representing X.

158

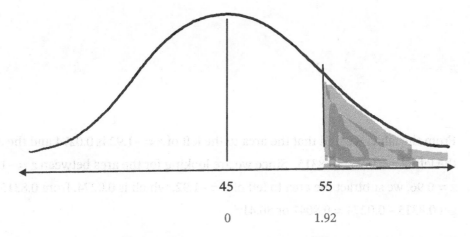

45   55

0   1.92

$$z = \frac{X - \mu}{\sigma} = \frac{55 - 45}{5.2} = 1.92$$

From the table, we find that the area to the left of $z = 1.92$ is 0.9726. Since we are looking for the area to the right of $z = 1.92$, we subtract the area to left of $z = 1.92$, which is 0.9726, from 1.000 (or 1). We get $1.000 - 0.9726 = 0.0274$ or 2.74%.

Therefore, the probability that the person takes more than 55 minutes to get to work is 2.74%.

b. If a person driving to work is randomly selected, find the following probability that the person takes between 35 and 50 minutes to get to work.

We draw the normal curve. In this question, we are finding the probability so we must convert both X values to z. Then refer to the z table to find the cumulative area to the left of each z value representing each X.

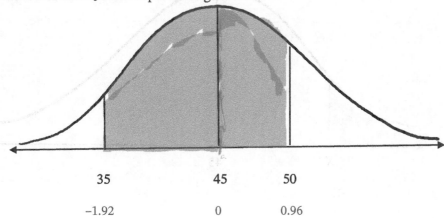

35   45   50

−1.92   0   0.96

159

$$z = \frac{X-\mu}{\sigma} = \frac{35-45}{5.2} = -1.92 \qquad z = \frac{X-\mu}{\sigma} = \frac{50-45}{5.2} = 0.96$$

From the table, we find that the area to the left of $z = -1.92$ is 0.0274 and the area to the left of $z = 0.96$ is 0.8315. Since we are looking for the area between $z = -1.92$ and $z = 0.96$, we subtract the area to left of $z = -1.92$, which is 0.0274, from 0.8315. We get $0.8315 - 0.0274 = 0.8041$ or 80.41%

Therefore, the probability that the person takes between 35 and 50 minutes to get to work is 80.41%.

c. The people that are at the bottom 14% of the travel time distribution are less stressed since their travel time to work is less than that of the upper 86%. Find the cutoff for the bottom 14%.

We draw the normal curve. In this question, we are given the probability in order to find the cutoff score which is X. First refer to the z table to find the negative z value that corresponds to the cumulative area to the left of it which is 14% or 0.1400. The closest area is 0.1401, and the z value is –1.08. Then, solve for X using the modified formula.

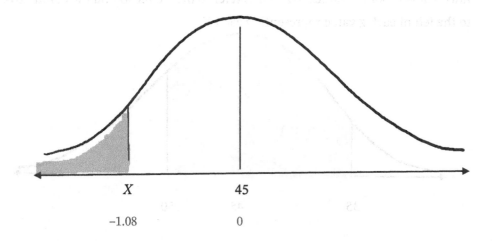

160

$$X = z\sigma + \mu = (-1.08)(5.2) + 45 = -5.616 + 45 = 39.384 \approx 39$$

Therefore, the 14% cutoff before feeling more stressed is about 39 minutes.

d. Find the cutoff times for the middle 62%.

We draw the normal curve. In this question, we are given the probability for the middle area with two cutoff scores, one below and one above the mean. To make a distinction we can call one X_{MIN} for the minimum cutoff and X_{MAX} for the maximum. [NOTE: The subscripts can be named differently: X_1 and X_2 or X_a and X_b as long as a distinction is made since there are two values of X.]

If we subtract 100% – 62%, we get a total of 38% for the two tail areas. Since the curve is symmetric with respect to the mean, we can divide the total tail area by 2 giving us 19% in each tail. So the area to the left of the negative z value is 19% or 0.1900. We refer to the negative z values to find the negative z value that corresponds to the cumulative area to the left of it which is 19% or 0.1900. The closest area is 0.1894 so the negative z value is –0.88. By symmetry, the positive z value is 0.88. Then, solve for each X using the modified formula.

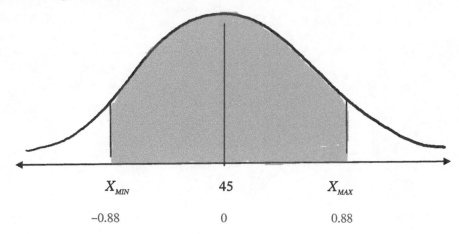

$$X_{MIN} = z\sigma + \mu = (-0.88)(5.2) + 45 = -4.576 + 45 = 40.424 \approx 40$$

$$X_{MAX} = z\sigma + \mu = (0.88)(5.2) + 45 = 4.576 + 45 = 49.576 \approx 50$$

Therefore, the middle 62% cutoff times are between 40 and 50 minutes. In other words, the middle 62% falls within the interval $39 < X < 55$ minutes.

Your Turn to Practice

At a community college with only commuter students, a study determined that the mean travel time for the students in the morning from their homes to the campus is 25 minutes with a standard deviation of 4.5 minutes. Assume the travel time is normally distributed. Find each of the following.

1. Find the probability that a randomly selected student takes less than 20 minutes to get to the campus in the morning.

162

2. Find the probability that a randomly selected student takes more than 35 minutes to get to the campus in the morning.

3. Find the probability that a randomly selected student takes more than 15 minutes to get to the campus in the morning.

4. Find the probability that a randomly selected student takes between 10 to 40 minutes to get to the campus in the morning.

5. The students that have the longest 25% of travel times arrive rushed to their classes. Find the cutoff for the top 25%.

6. The students that are at the have the shortest 20% of travel times get to find better seating in the classes by arriving earlier. Find the cutoff for the bottom 20%.

7. Find the cutoff times for the middle 84%.

6.4 Use the Correction for Continuity to Approximate the Binomial using the Normal

In Section 5.3, we discussed the binomial distribution, which is a discrete distribution. The values for binomial probabilities were calculated for smaller values of *n*. For larger values of *n*, we may use the normal approximation to the binomial distribution given that the following conditions are satisfied:

i.   The conditions of a binomial experiment apply (refer to Section 5.3).

ii. $np \geq 5$ and $nq \geq 5$, where *p* represents the probability of success and $q = 1 - p$ represents the probability of failure

We can then apply the correction for continuity (continuity correction), allowing us to use the continuous normal distribution to approximate the discrete binomial distribution.

The continuity correction uses a correction of ± 0.5 for the discrete values of *X*.

165

The continuity correction rules are as follows:

- Probability of **Exactly** X number of successes: $P(X = \text{number})$
  - For the normal approximation, use $P(\text{number} - 0.5 < X < \text{number} + 0.5)$
- Probability of **at least** X number of successes: $P(X \geq \text{number})$
  - For the normal approximation, use $P(X > \text{number} - 0.5)$
- Probability of **more than** X number of successes: $P(X > \text{number})$
  - For the normal approximation use, $P(X > \text{number} + 0.5)$
- Probability of **at most** X number of successes: $P(X \leq \text{number})$
  - For the normal approximation use, $P(X < \text{number} + 0.5)$
- Probability of **less than** X number of successes: $P(X < \text{number})$
  - For the normal approximation use, $P(X < \text{number} - 0.5)$

Example:

Sixty-four percent of college students say they like statistics more than algebra. In a survey of 100 randomly chosen college students, find the probability of each:

a. That exactly 75 like statistics more than algebra.

$n = 100 \;\; p = 0.64$ and $q = 1 - 0.64 = 0.36$

    i. This is a binomial experiment since all four conditions apply.

    Condition #1 is satisfied. The response to the question in this survey is either **yes** or **no**. We can assign the success to be answering **yes**, so a failure is answering **no**. Alternatively, we can assign answering **no** as the success of the experiment, thus assigning failure for a **no** answer. In either scenario, there are only two possible outcomes.

    Condition #2 is satisfied. The total number of trials is 100, because there are 100 randomly chosen college students. $n = 100$

<u>Condition #3 is satisfied.</u> It is reasonable to assume in this survey that each randomly selected college student's answer is independent of the other. Thus, each trial is independent.

<u>Condition #4 is satisfied.</u> Assuming success is answering **yes**, the success rate is $p = 0.64$ and remains the same throughout the entire survey. Consequently, the failure rate $q = 0.36$ also remains the same throughout the survey.

ii. Verify that $np \geq 5$ and $nq \geq 5$.

First, we find that $np = (100)(0.64) = 64 \geq 5$ and $nq = (100)(0.36) = 36 \geq 5$ so we can use the normal approximation to the binomial distribution with the following mean and standard deviation:

$$\mu = np = (100)(0.64) = 64 \text{ and } \sigma = \sqrt{npq} = \sqrt{(100)(0.64)(0.36)} = \sqrt{23.04} = 4.8$$

Find $P(X = 75)$. Using the continuity correction for the binomial we are finding $P(74.5 < X < 75.5)$

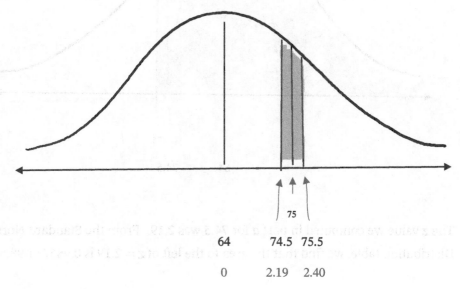

In this question, we are finding the probability so we must convert both X values to z. Then refer to the z table to find the cumulative area to the left of each z value representing each X.

$$z = \frac{X - \mu}{\sigma} = \frac{74.5 - 64}{4.8} \approx 2.19 \qquad z = \frac{X - \mu}{\sigma} = \frac{75.5 - 64}{4.8} \approx 2.40$$

From the table, we find that the area to the left of $z = 2.19$ is 0.9857 and the area to the left of $z = 2.40$ is 0.9918. Since we are looking for the area between $z = 2.19$ and $z = 2.40$, we subtract the area to left of $z = 2.19$, which is 0.9857, from 0.9918. We get $0.9918 - 0.9857 = 0.0061$ or 0.61%

Therefore, the probability that exactly 75 out of 100 randomly chosen college students like statistics more than algebra is 0.61%.

b. That fewer than 75 like statistics more than algebra.

Find $P(X < 75)$. Using the continuity correction for the binomial, find $P(X < 74.5)$

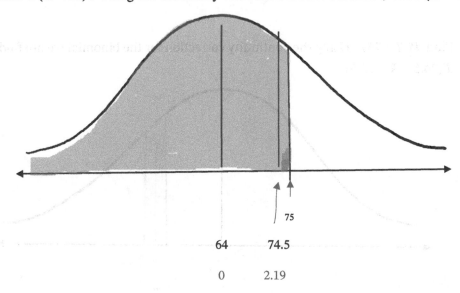

The z value we computed in part a for 74.5 was 2.19. From the Standard Normal Distribution table, we find that the area to the left of $z = 2.19$ is 0.9857 or 98.57%.

168

Therefore, the probability that fewer than 75 out of 100 randomly chosen college students like statistics more than algebra is 98.57%.

c. That at most 60 like statistics more than algebra.

Find $P(X \leq 60)$. Using the continuity correction for the binomial, find $P(X < 60.5)$

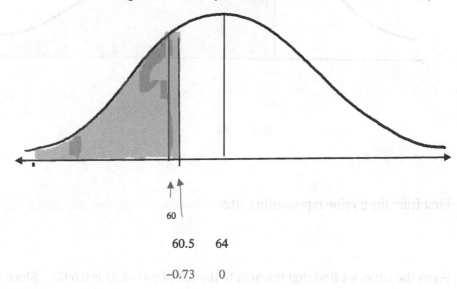

60

60.5   64

−0.73   0

First from the z value representing 60.5: $z = \dfrac{X - \mu}{\sigma} = \dfrac{60.5 - 64}{4.8} \approx -0.73$

From the table, we find that the area to the left of $z = -0.73$ is 0.2327 or 23.27%.
Therefore, the probability that at most 60 out of 100 randomly chosen college students like statistics more than algebra is 23.27%.

169

d. That more than 50 like statistics more than algebra.

Find $P(X > 50)$. Using the continuity correction for the binomial, find $P(X > 50.5)$

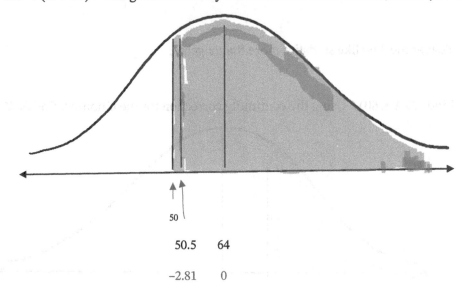

50

50.5   64

−2.81   0

First from the z value representing 50.5: $z = \dfrac{X - \mu}{\sigma} = \dfrac{50.5 - 64}{4.8} \approx -2.81$

From the table, we find that the area to the left of $z = -2.81$ is 0.0025. Since we are looking for the area to the right of $z = -2.81$, we subtract the area to left of $z = -2.81$, which is 0.0025, from 1.000 (or 1). We get 1.000 − 0.0025 = 0.9975 or 99.75%.

Therefore, the probability that more than 50 out of 100 randomly chosen college students like statistics more than algebra is 99.75%.

Your Turn to Practice

Seventy-five percent of Central Florida residents visit Walt Disney World at least once every two years. Fifty random Central Florida residents are selected. Find the probability of each:

1. That at least 40 residents visit Walt Disney World at least once every two years.

2. That fewer than 30 residents visit Walt Disney World at least once every two years.

3. That at most 28 residents visit Walt Disney World at least once every two years.

4. That exactly 30 residents visit Walt Disney World at least once every two years.

5. That more than 35 residents visit Walt Disney World at least once every two years.

Chapter 7 Confidence Intervals

7.1 Defining Notation used with Confidence Intervals

In Chapter 3, we defined how the Greek letters μ, σ, and σ^2 are used in statistics to represent the population values of the mean, standard deviation, and variance, respectively. The population symbols are also called *parameters* while the sample notations are called *statistics*. Thus, $\overline{X}$, s, and s^2 are the symbols for the sample values for the sample mean, sample standard deviation, and sample variance, respectively. In Chapter 5, for the binomial distribution we define p as the probability of success. We can further define p as the probability of success in a population, thus p is a parameter. Then the probability of success in a sample can be defined by the statistic $\hat{p}$ (called "p-hat"). The relationship between p and $\hat{p}$ is the same as that with μ and $\overline{X}$. In this chapter, we will discuss how the sample values will be used as estimators of the parameters. We will use the z table (Table E: The Standard Normal Distribution) and introduce the t table (Table F: The t Distribution) to construct confidence intervals of a specific parameter.

In the previous chapter we used the z table (Table E) for normally distributed data to find either the probability (or area under the curve) or to find the cutoff score for a given probability value. For the standard normal distribution where $\mu = 0$ and $\sigma = 1$, the cutoff scores for specific probabilities were the z values found on the table. For the cases where we were finding the two cutoff z values, one negative and one positive that were equidistant from the mean $\mu = 0$ (thus leaving equal area in each tail), we refer to the negative portion of the table by using the area to the left of the negative z value. Using symmetry, the upper cutoff score or the positive z value has the opposite sign. *The other option for finding the positive z value is to subtract 1 minus the area to the right of the positive z value and refer to the positive portion of the table by using the area to the left of the positive z value.*

The two cutoff z values thus separate the middle area (or percentage) from that of the two tails of equal area of the curve. In Chapter 8, we will further discuss the two tails when discussing a two-tailed test for hypothesis testing.

The total area of the two tails that have equal area is denoted as the Greek letter α. By symmetry, each tail area is equal to $\frac{\alpha}{2}$. The specific z known as the critical value for the two tailed cases is denoted by $z_{\alpha/2}$. The subscript is used since we have the two tails, each of area $\alpha/2$, and the z means the z value. The value $z_{\alpha/2}$ that is used in the formula for confidence intervals is a positive value. Therefore, $z_{\alpha/2}$ is equal to the cutoff positive z value for the right tail. The cutoff negative z value for the left tail is represented with the negative symbol in front of $z_{\alpha/2}$, in other words $-z_{\alpha/2}$. See below.

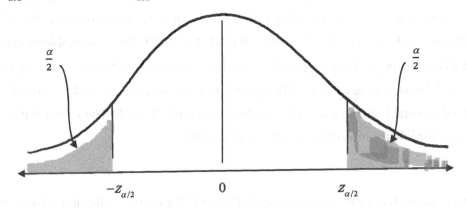

The percentage in the middle of the curve between $-z_{\alpha/2}$ and $z_{\alpha/2}$ is known as our *confidence level*. Therefore, the confidence level is $1 - \alpha$. If $\alpha = 0.02$, the confidence level is $1 - 0.02 = 0.98$ or 98%. The same holds true in reverse. If we have a 95% confidence level, then $\alpha = 100\% - 95\% = 1 - 0.95 = 0.05$ or 5%. Consequently $\frac{\alpha}{2} = \frac{0.05}{2} = 0.025$ or 2.5%. The confidence interval is the interval estimate of our parameter (or population value) based on a sample using a specified confidence level of the estimate. When the confidence level is 95%, we refer to the confidence based on this percentage as the 95% confidence interval. Thus, for a 95% confidence interval we are 95% confident that our parameter will fall within this interval estimate. In Section 7.4, we will construct confidence intervals.

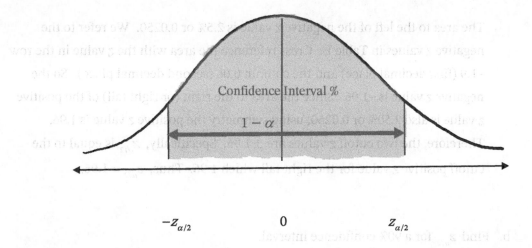

Confidence Interval %

$1 - \alpha$

$-z_{\alpha/2}$ 0 $z_{\alpha/2}$

Example:

Find the critical value $z_{\alpha/2}$ for each of the following.

    a. Find $z_{\alpha/2}$ for a 95% confidence interval.

        Since we have a 95% confidence level, $\alpha = 100\% - 95\% = 1 - 0.95 = 0.05$ or 5%.
        Consequently $\frac{\alpha}{2} = \frac{0.05}{2} = 0.025$ or 2.5% in each tail.

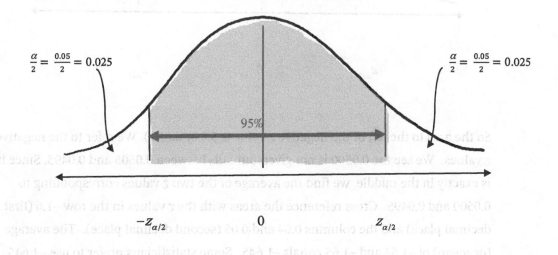

$\frac{\alpha}{2} = \frac{0.05}{2} = 0.025$

$\frac{\alpha}{2} = \frac{0.05}{2} = 0.025$

95%

$-z_{\alpha/2}$ 0 $z_{\alpha/2}$

The area to the left of the negative z value is 2.5% or 0.0250. We refer to the negative z values in Table E. Cross reference the area with the z value in the row –1.9 (first decimal place) and the column 0.06 (second decimal place). So the negative z value is –1.96. Since the area to the right (or right tail) of the positive z value is also 2.50% or 0.0250, using symmetry the positive z value is 1.96. Therefore, the two cutoff z values are ± 1.96. Specifically, $z_{\alpha/2}$ is equal to the cutoff positive z value for the right tail which 1.96. Thus, $z_{\alpha/2} = 1.96$.

b. Find $z_{\alpha/2}$ for a 90% confidence interval.

Since we have a 90% confidence level, $\alpha = 100\% - 90\% = 1 - 0.90 = 0.10$ or 10%. Consequently $\frac{\alpha}{2} = \frac{0.10}{2} = 0.05$ or 5% at each tail.

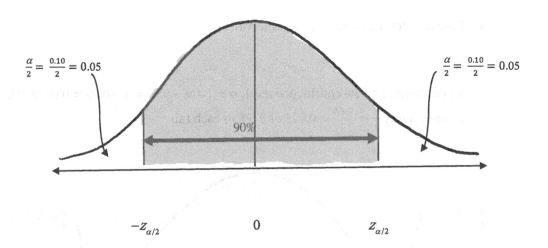

So the area to the left of the negative z value is 5% or 0.0500. We refer to the negative z values. We see the 0.0500 is not given but falls between 0.0505 and 0.0495. Since it is exactly in the middle, we find the average of the two z values corresponding to 0.0500 and 0.0495. Cross reference the areas with the z values in the row –1.6 (first decimal place) and the columns 0.04 and 0.05 (second decimal place). The average (or mean) of –1.64 and –1.65 equals –1.645. Some statisticians prefer to use –1.645. Others prefer rounding it off to two decimal places such that the negative z value is –

178

1.65 which is the value we will use in our applications. Since the area to the right (right tail) of the positive z value is also 5%, using symmetry, the positive z value is 1.65. Therefore, the two z values are ± 1.65. Specifically, $z_{\alpha/2}$ is equal to the cutoff positive z value for the right tail which is 1.65. Thus, $z_{\alpha/2} = 1.65$.

Your Turn to Practice

Find the critical value $z_{\alpha/2}$ for each of the following.

1. Find $z_{\alpha/2}$ for a 92% confidence interval.

2. Find $z_{\alpha/2}$ for a 99% confidence interval.

3. Find $z_{\alpha/2}$ for a 96% confidence interval.

4. Find $z_{\alpha/2}$ for a 98% confidence interval.

5. Find $z_{\alpha/2}$ for a 93% confidence interval.

6. Find $z_{\alpha/2}$ for a 94% confidence interval.

7. Find $z_{\alpha/2}$ for a 97% confidence interval.

7.2 Distinguishing between Parameters and Statistics

As we discussed in Section 7.1, a confidence interval is the interval estimate that contains the parameter (or population value) for a specific confidence level. The parameter can represent the population or "true" value for any one of these measures: mean, standard deviation, variance, proportion (or percentage) of success. *NOTE: We will use proportion to refer to the proportion (or percentage) of success.* Since this is a binomial, we use p to represent the proportion assuming success, and q will be the failure rate of the population. The statistics (or sample values) will be the estimators of the parameters. As such, we refer to a statistic as a point estimate of the parameter. Below is a chart showing the population symbols (or parameters) with their point estimates (or statistics).

	Parameter	Statistic or Point estimate
Mean (or average)	μ	$\bar{x}$
Standard deviation	σ	s
Variance	σ^2	s^2
Proportion (represents success rate)	p	$\hat{p}$
Failure rate	$q = 1 - p$	$\hat{q} = 1 - \hat{p}$

181

Examples:

Find the point estimate.

a. In a sample of 500 commuter students, the mean time spent commuting daily was 2 hours. The population standard deviation is 15 minutes (or 0.25 hour). Find the point estimate for the population mean.

The point estimate is the sample average $\bar{x} = 2$.

b. Some healthcare professionals feel that they are underpaid given the long hours that they work. In a study with a group of 15 heath care professionals, the average yearly salary was \$52,000 with a standard deviation was 4,153. Find the point estimate for the mean of the population.

The point estimate is the sample mean $\bar{x} = 52,000$.

c. A survey of 200 Floridians found that 40% were born outside of Florida. Find the point estimate $\hat{p}$ for the population proportion. Also, find the value of $\hat{q}$.

The point estimate is the sample proportion $\hat{p} = 0.40$. Therefore, $\hat{q} = 1 - \hat{p} = 0.60$.

Your Turn to Practice

Find the point estimate.

1. In a study of 100 middle school children, the mean number of hours weekly spent playing video games was 15 hours with a standard deviation of 2 hours. Find the point estimate for the true mean number of hours weekly that middle school children spent playing video games.

2. A group of 90 community college students were asked if they plan to transfer to a four-year university upon completion of their Associate in Arts degree. Eight-one of them stated that they plan to transfer to a four-year university upon completion of their Associate in Arts degree. Find the point estimate $\hat{p}$ for the population proportion. Also, find the value of $\hat{q}$.

3. A survey of 40 parents found that 80% were worried about their kids spending too much time texting. Find the point estimate $\hat{p}$ for the population proportion. Also, find the value of $\hat{q}$.

4. From a study conducted of 250 online shoppers, an online retailer determined that the average amount of time shoppers who shop online at night is 20 minutes. The population standard is assumed to be 3 minutes. Find the point estimate for the population mean.

183

7.3 Read and Interpret the *t* table

For normally distributed data, we have been using the critical values $z_{\alpha/2}$ from the standard normal distribution. Assuming the population standard σ is known, the $z_{\alpha/2}$ values are used to maintain a certain confidence level. However, when σ is unknown, we must use the sample standard deviation, *s*, which affects the critical value specifically for small samples. To "stabilize" the confidence level or keep the specified confidence interval the same particularly with small samples, the critical values will vary based on the sample size. For normal distributions, these critical values are obtained from the *t* distribution (also referred to as the Student's *t* distribution). We replace $z_{\alpha/2}$ with $t_{\alpha/2}$. The larger the sample, the closer the distribution is to the standard normal distribution, so the critical value $t_{\alpha/2}$ approaches the critical value $z_{\alpha/2}$ for that confidence level. The critical values from the *t* distribution are determined by "degrees of freedom." The degrees of freedom determine the shape of the *t* distribution. When working with a single mean for confidence intervals and hypothesis tests, which will be see in the next chapter, the degrees of freedom (d.f.) equal one less than the sample size so that d.f. = *n* – 1. When working with two or more populations, the degrees of freedom are computed differently.

[Note: Within the scope of this book, we are only working with a single mean so we will only use d.f. = n – 1.]

To find the critical $t_{\alpha/2}$ values, we must compute the d.f. and then cross reference the d.f. with the corresponding confidence level. We observe that the critical values from the *t* table (Table F) are for the right tail. We use symmetry to obtain the left tail value.

184

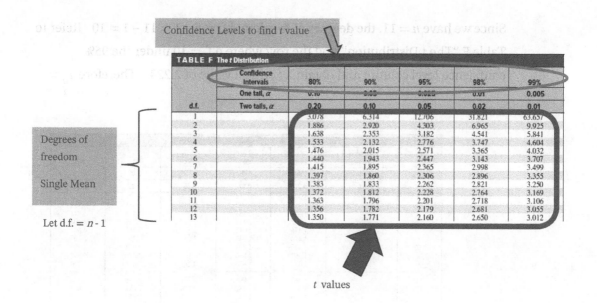

Confidence Levels to find *t* value

TABLE F The *t* Distribution

d.f.	Confidence Intervals	80%	90%	95%	98%	99%
	One tail, α	0.10	0.05	0.025	0.01	0.005
	Two tails, α	0.20	0.10	0.05	0.02	0.01
1		3.078	6.314	12.706	31.821	63.657
2		1.886	2.920	4.303	6.965	9.925
3		1.638	2.353	3.182	4.541	5.841
4		1.533	2.132	2.776	3.747	4.604
5		1.476	2.015	2.571	3.365	4.032
6		1.440	1.943	2.447	3.143	3.707
7		1.415	1.895	2.365	2.998	3.499
8		1.397	1.860	2.306	2.896	3.355
9		1.383	1.833	2.262	2.821	3.250
10		1.372	1.812	2.228	2.764	3.169
11		1.363	1.796	2.201	2.718	3.106
12		1.356	1.782	2.179	2.681	3.055
13		1.350	1.771	2.160	2.650	3.012

Degrees of freedom

Single Mean

Let d.f. = n - 1

t values

Examples:

Find the critical value $t_{\alpha/2}$ for each of the following confidence intervals for a single mean.

a. Find $t_{\alpha/2}$ with $n = 11$ for a 95% confidence interval.

Since we have a 95% confidence level, $\alpha = 100\% - 95\% = 1 - 0.95 = 0.05$ or 5%. Consequently $\frac{\alpha}{2} = \frac{0.05}{2} = 0.025$ or 2.5% at each tail.

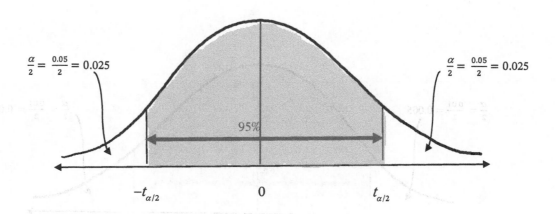

$\frac{\alpha}{2} = \frac{0.05}{2} = 0.025$ $\frac{\alpha}{2} = \frac{0.05}{2} = 0.025$

95%

$-t_{\alpha/2}$ 0 $t_{\alpha/2}$

Since we have $n = 11$, the degrees of freedom d.f. $= n - 1 = 11 - 1 = 10$. Refer to Table F "The t Distribution" and the row where d.f. $= 10$ under the 95% confidence level column and obtain a t critical value of 2.228. Therefore $t_{\frac{\alpha}{2}} = 2.228$.

TABLE F The *t* Distribution						
	Confidence intervals	80%	90%	95%	98%	99%
	One tail, α	0.10	0.05	0.025	0.01	0.005
d.f.	Two tails, α	0.20	0.10	0.05	0.02	0.01
1		3.078	6.314	12.706	31.821	63.657
2		1.886	2.920	4.303	6.965	9.925
3		1.638	2.353	3.182	4.541	5.841
4		1.533	2.132	2.776	3.747	4.604
5		1.476	2.015	2.571	3.365	4.032
6		1.440	1.943	2.447	3.143	3.707
7		1.415	1.895	2.365	2.998	3.499
8		1.397	1.860	2.306	2.896	3.355
9		1.383	1.833	2.262	2.821	3.250
10		1.372	1.812	2.228	2.764	3.169
11		1.363	1.796	2.201	2.718	3.106
12		1.356	1.782	2.179	2.681	3.055
13		1.350	1.771	2.160	2.650	3.012

b. Find $t_{\alpha/2}$ with $n = 6$ for a 99% confidence interval.

Since we have a 99% confidence level, $\alpha = 100\% - 99\% = 1 - 0.99 = 0.01$ or 1%. Consequently $\frac{\alpha}{2} = \frac{0.01}{2} = 0.005$ or 0.5% in each tail.

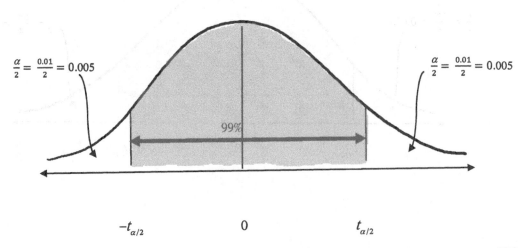

$\frac{\alpha}{2} = \frac{0.01}{2} = 0.005$ $\frac{\alpha}{2} = \frac{0.01}{2} = 0.005$

99%

$-t_{\alpha/2}$ 0 $t_{\alpha/2}$

186

Since we have $n = 6$, the degrees of freedom d.f. $= n - 1 = 6 - 1 = 5$. Refer to the row where d.f. $= 5$ under the 99% confidence level column and obtain a t critical value of 4.032. Therefore $t_{\alpha/2} = 4.032$.

TABLE F The t Distribution

d.f.	Confidence intervals	80%	90%	95%	98%	99%
	One tail, α	0.10	0.05	0.025	0.01	0.005
	Two tails, α	0.20	0.10	0.05	0.02	0.01
1		3.078	6.314	12.706	31.821	63.657
2		1.886	2.920	4.303	6.965	9.925
3		1.638	2.353	3.182	4.541	5.841
4		1.533	2.132	2.776	3.747	4.604
5		1.476	2.015	2.571	3.365	4.032
6		1.440	1.943	2.447	3.143	3.707
7		1.415	1.895	2.365	2.998	3.499
8		1.397	1.860	2.306	2.896	3.355
9		1.383	1.833	2.262	2.821	3.250
10		1.372	1.812	2.228	2.764	3.169
11		1.363	1.796	2.201	2.718	3.106
12		1.356	1.782	2.179	2.681	3.055
13		1.350	1.771	2.160	2.650	3.012

c. Find $t_{\alpha/2}$ with $n = 54$ for a 90% confidence interval.

Since we have a 90% confidence level, $\alpha = 100\% - 90\% = 1 - 0.90 = 0.10$ or 10%. Consequently $\frac{\alpha}{2} = \frac{0.10}{2} = 0.05$ or 5% in each tail.

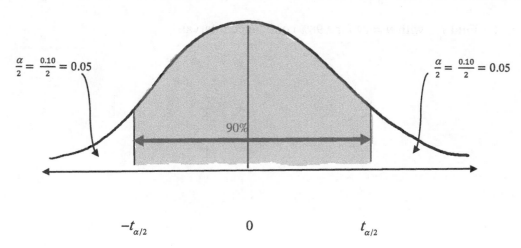

$$\frac{\alpha}{2} = \frac{0.10}{2} = 0.05 \qquad \qquad \frac{\alpha}{2} = \frac{0.10}{2} = 0.05$$

90%

$-t_{\alpha/2}$ \qquad 0 \qquad $t_{\alpha/2}$

187

Since we have $n = 54$, the degrees of freedom d.f. $= n - 1 = 54 - 1 = 53$. Refer to the row where d.f. $= 53$ under the 90% confidence level column. There is no entry for d.f. $= 53$ in the table. The two values given are 50 and 55. We will use the conservative approach of taking the value associated with the d.f.—we always round the degrees of freedom value down and do not round d.f. to the closer value. In other words, use d.f. $= 50$ even though 53 is closer to 55. Refer to the row where d.f. $= 50$ under the 90% confidence level column, and obtain a t critical value of 1.676. Therefore $t_{\alpha/2} = 1.676$.

Confidence Intervals	80%	90%	95%	98%	99%
One tail, α	0.10	0.05	0.025	0.01	0.005
d.f. Two tails, α	0.20	0.10	0.05	0.02	0.01
30		1.310	1.697	2.042	2.457	2.750
32		1.309	1.694	2.037	2.449	2.738
34		1.307	1.691	2.032	2.441	2.728
36		1.306	1.688	2.028	2.434	2.719
38		1.304	1.686	2.024	2.429	2.712
40		1.303	1.684	2.021	2.423	2.704
45		1.301	1.679	2.014	2.412	2.690
50		1.299	1.676	2.009	2.403	2.678
55		1.297	1.673	2.004	2.396	2.668
60		1.296	1.671	2.000	2.390	2.660

d.f. = 53 which falls between 50 and 55.

Use the smaller d.f. which is 50

Your Turn to Practice

Find the critical value $t_{\alpha/2}$ for each of the following confidence intervals for a single mean.

1. Find $t_{\alpha/2}$ with $n = 24$ for a 98% confidence interval.

2. Find $t_{\alpha/2}$ with $n = 5$ for a 99% confidence interval.

3. Find $t_{\alpha/2}$ with $n = 85$ for a 95% confidence interval.

4. Find $t_{\alpha/2}$ with $n = 30$ for a 90% confidence interval.

5. Find $t_{\alpha/2}$ with $n = 40$ for a 98% confidence interval.

We have determined how to find the critical values for $z_{\alpha/2}$ and $t_{\alpha/2}$ so now we need to determine when to use the z value or when to use the t value. When working with a single mean, the sample size of 30 is used as the cutoff as to when a sample is considered small. The t distribution table can also be used to find critical z values for specific confidence levels 80%, 90%, 95%, 98% and 99%. If any other confidence level not appearing on this table is used, we refer to the z table.

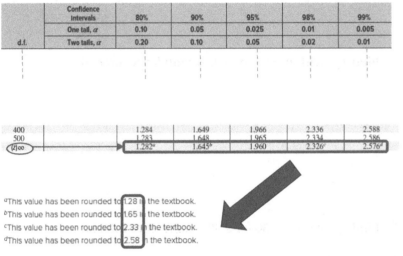

	Confidence Intervals	80%	90%	95%	98%	99%
	One tail, α	0.10	0.05	0.025	0.01	0.005
d.f.	Two tails, α	0.20	0.10	0.05	0.02	0.01

400	1.284	1.649	1.966	2.336	2.588
500	1.283	1.648	1.965	2.334	2.586
(2)∞	1.282[a]	1.645[b]	1.960	2.326[c]	2.576[d]

[a]This value has been rounded to 1.28 in the textbook.
[b]This value has been rounded to 1.65 in the textbook.
[c]This value has been rounded to 2.33 in the textbook.
[d]This value has been rounded to 2.58 in the textbook.

z values rounded to two decimal places

Examples:

Determine whether to use $z_{\alpha/2}$ or $t_{\alpha/2}$. Find the critical value.

a. Given $n = 8$ and $s = 3$ for a 95% confidence interval.

Use $t_{\alpha/2}$ since σ is unknown, s is given and $n \leq 30$.

Since we have $n = 8$, the degrees of freedom d.f. $= n - 1 = 8 - 1 = 7$. Refer to the row where d.f. $= 7$ under the 95% confidence level column and obtain a t critical value of 2.365. Therefore $t_{\alpha/2} = 2.365$.

TABLE F The *t* Distribution						
	Confidence Intervals	80%	90%	95%	98%	99%
	One tail, α	0.10	0.05	0.025	0.01	0.005
d.f.	Two tails, α	0.20	0.10	0.05	0.02	0.01
1		3.078	6.314	12.706	31.821	63.657
2		1.886	2.920	4.303	6.965	9.925
3		1.638	2.353	3.182	4.541	5.841
4		1.533	2.132	2.776	3.747	4.604
5		1.476	2.015	2.571	3.365	4.032
6		1.440	1.943	2.447	3.143	3.707
7		1.415	1.895	2.365	2.998	3.499
8		1.397	1.860	2.306	2.896	3.355
9		1.383	1.833	2.262	2.821	3.250
10		1.372	1.812	2.228	2.764	3.169
11		1.363	1.796	2.201	2.718	3.106
12		1.356	1.782	2.179	2.681	3.055
13		1.350	1.771	2.160	2.650	3.012

b. Given $n = 10$ and $\sigma = 3$ for a 98% confidence interval.

Use $z_{\alpha/2}$ since σ is given. Since 98% can be found on the *t* table, we refer to the last row under the 98% column. We obtain a z critical value of 2.326 $\approx$ 2.33. Therefore $z_{\alpha/2} = 2.33$.

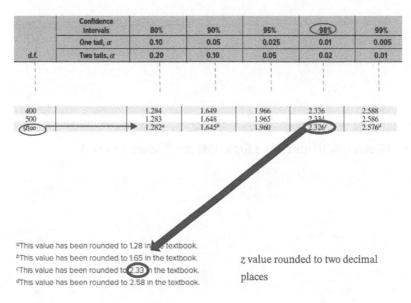

	Confidence Intervals	80%	90%	95%	98%	99%
	One tail, α	0.10	0.05	0.025	0.01	0.005
d.f.	Two tails, α	0.20	0.10	0.05	0.02	0.01
400		1.284	1.649	1.966	2.336	2.588
500		1.283	1.648	1.965	2.334	2.586
∞		1.282[a]	1.645[b]	1.960	2.326[c]	2.576[d]

[a]This value has been rounded to 1.28 in the textbook.
[b]This value has been rounded to 1.65 in the textbook.
[c]This value has been rounded to 2.33 in the textbook.
[d]This value has been rounded to 2.58 in the textbook.

z value rounded to two decimal places

c. Given $n = 29$ and $s = 10$ for a 99% confidence interval.

Use $t_{\alpha/2}$ since σ is unknown, s is given and $n \le 30$.

191

Since we have $n = 29$, the degrees of freedom d.f. $= n - 1 = 29 - 1 = 28$. Refer to the row where d.f. $= 28$ under the 99% confidence level column and obtain a t critical value of 2.763. Therefore $t_{\alpha/2} = 2.763$.

Your Turn to Practice

Determine whether to use $z_{\alpha/2}$ or $t_{\alpha/2}$. Find the critical value.

1. Given $n = 8$ and $s = 3$ for a 95% confidence interval.

2. Given $n = 10$ and $\sigma = 3$ for a 95% confidence interval.

3. Given $n = 29$ and $s = 10$ for a 99% confidence interval.

4. Given $n = 40$ and $\sigma = 5$ for a 90% confidence interval.

7.4 Finding Confidence Intervals and Finding Sample Sizes

In this section, we will construct confidence intervals for our parameter using the point estimate (or statistic) for that parameter. Once again, the confidence interval is the interval estimate that contains our parameter (or population value) within our specific confidence level. Since we are using a point estimate, there is some possible "error" between the point estimate and the parameter. The error is not a mistake, rather it is a value that takes into account random variation. The maximum error between the point estimate and the parameter is defined by the *margin of error*. We construct our confidence interval for the parameter as the value of the point estimate plus or minus the margin of error. In other words, we are certain % confident that the parameter falls in the interval:

$$\text{Point estimate} \pm \textit{Margin of Error}$$

or

$$\textit{Point estimate} - \boxed{\textit{Margin of Error}} < \textit{Parameter} < \textit{Point estimate} + \boxed{\textit{Margin of Error}}$$

If we let E = Margin of Error, we say:

$$\textit{Point estimate} - E < \textit{Parameter} < \textit{Point estimate} + E$$

If the parameter is the mean μ, then the point estimate is $\bar{x}$ and the margin of error is:

$$E = z_{\alpha/2}\left(\frac{\sigma}{\sqrt{n}}\right) \quad \text{or} \quad E = t_{\alpha/2}\left(\frac{s}{\sqrt{n}}\right)$$

So the confidence interval for the population mean is:

$$\bar{X} - z_{\alpha/2}\left(\frac{\sigma}{\sqrt{n}}\right) < \mu < \bar{X} + z_{\alpha/2}\left(\frac{\sigma}{\sqrt{n}}\right)$$

or

$$\bar{X} - t_{\alpha/2}\left(\frac{s}{\sqrt{n}}\right) < \mu < \bar{X} + t_{\alpha/2}\left(\frac{s}{\sqrt{n}}\right)$$

If the parameter is the proportion p, then the best point estimate is $\hat{p}$ and the margin of error is

$$E = z_{\alpha/2}\sqrt{\frac{\hat{p}\hat{q}}{n}}$$

194

So the confidence interval for the population proportion p is

$$\hat{p} - z_{\alpha/2}\sqrt{\frac{\hat{p}\hat{q}}{n}} < p < \hat{p} - z_{\alpha/2}\sqrt{\frac{\hat{p}\hat{q}}{n}}$$

Examples:

Find and interpret the confidence interval for each of the following.

    a. In a sample of 500 commuter students, the mean time spent commuting daily was 2 hours. The population standard deviation is 15 minutes (or 0.25 hour). Find the 95% confidence interval for the population average.

We are looking for the confidence interval for the population average, μ. The point estimate $\bar{x} = 2$. Use $z_{\alpha/2}$ since σ is given.

$$\bar{x} - z_{\alpha/2}\left(\frac{\sigma}{\sqrt{n}}\right) < \mu < \bar{x} + z_{\alpha/2}\left(\frac{\sigma}{\sqrt{n}}\right)$$

Since 95% can be found on the t table, we refer to the last row under the 95% column. We obtain a z critical value of $1.960 = 1.96$. Therefore $z_{\alpha/2} = 1.96$.

$$2 - 1.96\left(\frac{0.25}{\sqrt{500}}\right) < \mu < 2 + 1.96\left(\frac{0.25}{\sqrt{500}}\right)$$

$$2 - .02 < \mu < 2 + 0.2$$

$$1.8 < \mu < 2.2$$

Therefore, we are 95% confident that the population average time commuter students spent commuting daily is between 1.8 hours and 2.2 hours.

195

b. Some healthcare professionals feel that they are underpaid given the long hours that they work. In a study of a group of 15 heath care professionals, the average yearly salary was $52,000 with a standard deviation was 4,153. Find the 90% confidence interval of the mean yearly salary of the population of healthcare professionals.

We are looking for the confidence interval for the population average, μ. The point estimate $\bar{x} = 52,000$. Use $t_{\alpha/2}$ since σ is unknown, s is given and $n \leq 30$.

$$\bar{x} - t_{\alpha/2}\left(\frac{s}{\sqrt{n}}\right) < \mu < \bar{x} + t_{\alpha/2}\left(\frac{s}{\sqrt{n}}\right)$$

Since we have $n = 15$, the degrees of freedom d.f. $= n - 1 = 15 - 1 = 14$. Refer to the row where d.f. $= 14$ under the 90% confidence level column and obtain a t critical value of 1.761. Therefore $t_{\alpha/2} = 1.761$.

$$52000 - 1.761\left(\frac{4153}{\sqrt{15}}\right) < \mu < 52000 + 1.761\left(\frac{4153}{\sqrt{15}}\right)$$

$$52000 - 1888.32 < \mu < 52000 + 1888.32$$

$$50,111.68 < \mu < 53,888.32$$

So, we can say with 90% confidence that the interval between $50,111.68 and $53,888.32 does contain the population mean yearly salary based on a sample of 15 healthcare professionals.

c. A survey of 200 Floridians found that 40% were born outside of Florida. Find the 99% confidence interval of the population proportion.

We are looking for the confidence interval for the population proportion, p. The best point estimate is $\hat{p} = 0.40$. Therefore, $\hat{q} = 1 - \hat{p} = 0.60$.

$$\hat{p} - z_{\alpha/2}\sqrt{\frac{\hat{p}\hat{q}}{n}} < p < \hat{p} + z_{\alpha/2}\sqrt{\frac{\hat{p}\hat{q}}{n}}$$

Since 99% can be found on the t table, we refer to the last row under the 95% column. We obtain a z critical value of $2.576 \approx 2.58$. Therefore $z_{\alpha/2} = 2.58$.

$$0.40 - 2.58\sqrt{\frac{(0.40)(0.60)}{200}} < p < 0.40 + 2.58\sqrt{\frac{(0.40)(0.60)}{200}}$$

$$0.40 - 0.089 < p < 0.40 + 0.089$$

$$0.311 < p < 0.489$$

$$31.1\% < p < 48.9\%$$

So, we say with 99% confidence that the true percentage of Floridians born outside of Florida is between 31.1% and 48.9%.

197

Your Turn to Practice

Find and interpret the confidence interval for each of the following.

1. In a study of 10 middle school children, the mean number of hours weekly spent playing video games was 15 hours with a standard deviation of 2 hours. Find the 99% confidence interval for the true mean number of hours weekly spent playing video games.

2. A group of 90 community college students were asked if they plan to transfer to a four-year university upon completion of their Associate in Arts degree. Eight-one of them stated that they plan to transfer to a four-year university upon completion of their Associate in Arts degree. Find the 99% confidence interval of the population proportion.

3. A survey of 40 parents found that 80% were worried about their kids spending too much time texting. Estimate the true proportion of parents who are worried about their kids spending too much time texting at the 99% confidence interval.

4. From a study conducted of 250 online shoppers, an online retailer determined that the average amount of time shoppers who shop online at night is 20 minutes. The population standard is assumed to be 3 minutes. Estimate the population mean time spent shopping online at the 90% confidence level.

In the previous examples we constructed confidence intervals for the parameter given the sample size. Let's compare that to cases where we do not know the sample size and we wish to determine what the minimum sample size necessary will be at the specified confidence level with a defined margin of error. In such cases the unknown is n, so we can refer to the margin of error formulas for the mean and proportion and solve for n. Since n represents a whole number for the minimum sample size, if the answer is not a whole number, the rounding rule is to always round up to the next whole number.

For the mean, we assume that σ is known thus we refer to the formula $E = z_{\alpha/2}\left(\dfrac{\sigma}{\sqrt{n}}\right)$ and algebraically solve for n. The result is:

$$n = \left(\frac{z_{\alpha/2} \cdot \sigma}{E}\right)^2$$

Similarly for the proportion, we refer to the formula $E = z_{\alpha/2}\sqrt{\dfrac{\hat{p}\hat{q}}{n}}$ and algebraically solve for n. The result is:

$$n = \hat{p}\hat{q}\left(\frac{z_{\alpha/2}}{E}\right)^2$$

For the proportion if $\hat{p}$ is not given or approximated, then we use 0.5 for $\hat{p}$. We do so to ensure that the sample size is large enough to provide the most accurate prediction based on the confidence interval and error estimate. Consequently, $\hat{q} = 1 - \hat{p} = 1 - 0.5 = 0.5$

Examples:

Find the minimum sample size.

    a. A scientist wishes to determine the mean daily rain fall in inches during the summer in California. The scientist needs to determine how many days she will have to sample to be 95% confident and stay within a margin of error of 0.75

inches of rainfall from the population mean. Assume the standard deviation of the population is 1.2 inches of rainfall.

Since 95% can be found on the t table, we refer to the last row under the 95% column. We obtain a z critical value of $1.960 = 1.96$. Therefore $z_{\alpha/2} = 1.96$. The margin of error is $E = 0.75$. We are looking for the sample size n for a confidence interval for the population average, μ.

$$n = \left(\frac{z_{\alpha/2} \cdot \sigma}{E} \right)^2 = \left(\frac{(1.96)(1.2)}{0.75} \right)^2 = 9.834496 \text{ which is rounded up to 10.}$$

So we need a sample of 10 days.

b. A fast food restaurant chain is adding a new restaurant and conducted a study to determine the percentage of people who prefer to use the drive-thru during their lunch break. The proportion from that study was 64%. At the 90% confidence level, how large should the sample be to estimate the true proportion of those people with the margin of error within 2 percentage points from the population proportion?

Since 90% can be found on the t table, we refer to the last row under the 90% column. We obtain a z critical value of $1.645 \approx 1.65$. Therefore $z_{\alpha/2} = 1.65$. The margin of error is 2 percentage points, giving us $E = 0.02$. We are looking for the sample size n for a confidence interval for the population proportion, p.

Given $\hat{p} = 0.64$. Therefore, $\hat{q} = 1 - \hat{p} = 0.36$.

$$n = \hat{p}\hat{q} \left(\frac{z_{\alpha/2}}{E} \right)^2 = (0.64)(0.36) \left(\frac{1.65}{0.02} \right)^2 = 1{,}568.16 \text{ which is rounded up to 1,569.}$$

Thus, we need a sample of 1,569 people.

If $\hat{p}$ was not given, we would have used 0.5.

This would give us $n = \hat{p}\hat{q}\left(\dfrac{z_{\alpha/2}}{E}\right)^2 = (0.5)(0.5)\left(\dfrac{1.65}{0.02}\right)^2 = 1{,}701.5625$ which is rounded up to

1,702.

Thus, we need a sample of 1,702 people.

Your Turn to Practice

Find the minimum sample size.

1. A professor for a large class is worried that his students spend too little time studying. At the 98% confidence level, the professor needs to determine the sample size needed for a study that he will conduct on the average number of hours students study weekly for his entire class. He is assuming that the population standard deviation number of hours is 2.9 hours. The margin of error will be 2 hours from the true average.

2. The student government organization (SGA) at a local university is concerned that too many students are not informed politically. At the 99% confidence level, a study will be conducted to determine the true proportion of students who are not informed politically. The margin of error is to be within 3 percentage points from the population proportion. How large should the sample be if no previous estimate of the population proportion is available?

3. Using the same information given in number 2, how large should the sample be if an estimate from a previous study gave a sample proportion is 26%?

Chapter 8 Hypothesis Testing

8.1 Identify the Null and Alternative Hypothesis

In Chapter 7, we constructed confidence intervals to estimate the interval that, with a specified level of confidence, contains the parameter using the point estimate (or statistic) and the margin of error. In this chapter, we will use hypothesis testing to make an educated guess about the parameter value. In other words, the educated guess is not simply about an interval estimate, but rather a more precise guess as to a specific value for the parameter or the possible equality of two parameters from two populations.

First, we must define the two types of hypotheses used in hypothesis testing. They are called the null hypothesis and the alternative hypothesis. The null hypothesis, denoted H_o, refers to equality. This is the statement that there is no difference between the parameter and a specified number or no difference between two parameters.

Let's say we want to test if the mean of the population is equal to a specified value c. The null hypothesis, H_o, would be the mean of the population, μ, equals c. In other words, H_o: $\mu = c$. The alternate possibility is the mean of the population, μ, does not equal c. We call this statement the alternative hypothesis or H_1, which can also be denoted H_a. We can then summarize the two hypotheses as follows with the original claim (or conjecture) in this case being the equals:

$$H_o: \mu = c \text{(claim)}$$

$$H_1: \mu \neq c$$

It is important to note that the claim is not always with H_o. To determine where to place the claim, we must generalize the rules for H_o and H_1. If the claim is about equality or "no difference" then the claim is H_o. When the claim is to test if there is "a difference," then the claim is H_1. *Many researchers are testing that there is a difference between the parameter and*

204

the specified number, in which case the claim is H_1 and is referred to as the research hypothesis.

For the cases where there is one parameter and a specified value for that parameter, we have

H_0: There is no difference between the parameter and the number (EQUALITY)

H_1: There is a difference between the parameter and the number (INEQUALITY)

No difference means "equals." In general many statisticians, follow this approach of only assigning "=" to the H_0 statement. *NOTE: In some textbooks, the equality has been extended to all three forms that include the equals namely:* =, ≥, ≤. [You may use this option to initially set up the hypotheses and then modify H_0 to using only the "equals." The reason is that the hypothesis test is done at the point of equality, so we often use just the "equals" sign in the null hypothesis.] See below where the mean of the population, μ, is the parameter.

H_0: $\mu = c$	H_0: $\mu = c$ (originally $\mu \geq c$)	H_0: $\mu = c$ (originally $\mu \leq c$)
H_1: $\mu \neq c$	H_1: $\mu < c$	H_1: $\mu > c$

When constructing confidence intervals in the previous chapter, we worked with two tailed situations where $\propto$ is equal to the total area of the two tails. By symmetry, each tail area is equal to $\frac{\propto}{2}$, and the critical z and t values z were $z_{\alpha/2}$ and $t_{\alpha/2}$. In hypothesis testing, the test could be two-tailed or one-tailed (either left or right). The direction of the tail(s) is determined by the inequality in the alternative hypothesis.

H_1: $\mu \neq c$	H_1: $\mu < c$	H_1: $\mu > c$
TWO-TAILED	LEFT-TAILED	RIGHT-TAILED

These rules also apply to the cases where we have two or more parameters. If we are comparing two or more means, we can distinguish each mean by using subscripts 1, 2, 3,

205

etc., in other words the means would be: μ_1, μ_2, μ_3,... Similarly for proportions and standard deviations we could use p_1, p_2, p_3,... and σ_1, σ_2, σ_3,..., respectively.

Examples:

Find each claim (or conjecture), state the null hypothesis, H_o, and the alternative hypothesis, H_1. Identify the direction of the tail(s).

a. In an auditorium class, the average number of smokers is 23.

   Since the claim is about the average number of students, the parameter is μ and the claim is that $\mu = 23$. The claim is about equality or "no difference" then the claim is H_o. Thus, the alternative hypothesis is "not equal to."

   H_o: $\mu = 23$ (claim)

   H_1: $\mu \neq 23$

   Since H_1 is "not equal to," this is a two-tailed test.

b. In a large metropolitan area with various Internet providers, less than 60% of customers use a provider that offers Internet service bundled with TV service.

   Since the claim is about the percentage (or proportion) of customers, the parameter is p and the claim is that $p < 0.60$. The claim is about the inequality or "less than" thus the claim is H_1. Since H_1 is the alternative hypothesis, the negation is $p \geq 0.60$ but for the null hypothesis we only use "equals" thus, H_o is $p = 0.60$

   H_o: $p = 0.60$

   H_1: $p < 0.60$ (claim)

   Since H_1 is "less than," this is a left-tailed test.

c. At a bank, the standard deviation of the wait time for a teller is at most 3 minutes.

Since the claim is about the standard deviation of the wait time, the parameter is σ and the claim is that $\sigma \leq 3$. The claim is about "less than or equal to" which contains the equality then the claim is H_o, but for the null hypothesis we only use "equals" thus, H_o is $\sigma = 3$. Since H_1 is the alternative hypothesis, the negation of $\sigma \leq 3$ is the statement $\sigma > 3$.

H_o: $\sigma = 3$ (claim)

H_1: $\sigma > 3$

Since H_1 is "greater than," this is a right-tailed test.

d. When comparing two classes, there was no difference between the average number of absences in the 8 am class and the average number of absences in the 10 am class.

Since the claim is about the average number of absences, the parameter is μ. To distinguish between the two classes we use μ_1 and μ_2. We can assign μ_1 as the true average of the 8 am class, and μ_2 as the true average of the 10 am class. Since the subscripts for μ_1 and μ_2 are arbitrary, we can assign them to either class but we must specify that. The claim is about equality or "no difference" between the averages. Therefore, the claim $\mu_1 = \mu_2$ is H_o, and the alternative hypothesis is "not equal to."

H_o: $\mu_1 = \mu_2$ (claim)

H_1: $\mu_1 \neq \mu_2$

Since H_1 is "not equal to," this is a two-tailed test.

Your Turn to Practice

Find each claim (or conjecture), state the null hypothesis, H_o, and the alternative hypothesis, H_1. Identify the direction of the tail(s).

1. The true average wait time at a fast food drive-thru is more than 2 minutes.

2. The average number of cars in a household in the city of Springfield is 2 cars.

3. The standard deviation number of milligrams for one specific brand of antibiotics is at most 10 milligrams.

4. The percentage of students in a large statistics course taking notes with a tablet is at least 45%.

5. The average time spent shopping online for a specific retailer is less than 30 minutes.

6. The percentage of shoppers at a store that use the self-checkout system is no more than 30%.

7. The average number of Americans who subscribe to satellite TV is not the same as the average number who subscribe to an Internet streaming service for TV.

8.2 Hypothesis Testing: Traditional versus *P*-value Approach

In this section, we will introduce hypothesis testing specifically for a single mean using either the z or t critical values and test values. As such these statistical tests are referred to as the z test and the t test. As with confidence intervals, we determine whether to use z or t based on whether we are given the standard deviation of the population, σ. The total tail area is again represented by $\propto$, where $\frac{\propto}{2}$ is the area for each tail in a two-tailed test. In hypothesis testing, $\propto$ is referred to as the level of significance, which represents the maximum probability of making what is known as a Type I error. If you reject a statement that is true, that is a mistake. Since a hypothesis is an educated guess, there is always a risk of making a mistake when deciding to reject or not reject the null hypothesis. In statistics, we refer to the Type I error as the mistake that occurs when rejecting the null hypothesis when it was in fact true. Another mistake, referred to as a Type II error, occurs if you do not reject the null hypothesis when it was in fact false. The probability of a Type II error is represented by the Greek letter β. Since β is difficult to compute, in our work we will not work with it. However, we do set $\propto$ also known as the significance level when conducting hypothesis testing. For more information on these two types of error, refer to the textbook.

Typical values used for $\propto$ are 0.05, 0.10, 0.01, and 0.02. The researcher sets the level of significance for the test, with 0.05 usually utilized most often. Note that the significance level $\propto$ should be set before we conduct our hypothesis test. Also note that $\propto = 0.05$ is not "sacred," even though it is used most often.

There are two methods used in hypothesis testing: the traditional approach and the P-value approach. We will first apply the traditional approach and then the P-value approach.

Outline for Traditional Hypothesis Testing

1. State the hypotheses (null and alternative) and identify the claim.
2. Find the critical value(s) from the table.
3. Compute the test value using the formula.
4. Make the decision to reject or not reject the null hypothesis.
5. Summarize the results.

When we decide whether to reject or not reject H_o, we do not say reject or accept H_o. Consider the analogy of a jury verdict. A jury must determine if the defendant is guilty or not guilty. "Not guilty" does not mean innocence but rather insufficient evidence to prove guilt beyond a reasonable doubt. In statistics, we do not use the term "prove" as is used in the legal system, instead we either have enough evidence to reject H_o or not sufficient evidence to reject H_o. So, we cannot accept the null hypothesis ("innocent"), but we fail to reject the null hypothesis ("not guilty") when there is insufficient evidence to suggest the null hypothesis is false.

This final decision (or summary) about the claim is based on whether the claim was with H_o or H_1. An easy way to know to whether to reject or support the claim is to place the word *reject* before H_o and *support* before H_1.

So, the final summary will either be:

i.   Strong or significant evidence - <u>enough evidence to reject or support the claim</u>

ii.   Weak or insignificant evidence - <u>not enough evidence to reject or support the claim</u>

Examples:

Use the traditional method of hypothesis testing.

a.   At a university, a professor is concerned that students are spending too little time studying for her class. The average number of hours per week that all university students study for each class is 5 hours per week. In a random sample of 20 of her students, the average number of hours per week that those students were studying for her class was 4 hours. The population standard deviation was 90 minutes. At the 0.05 level of significance, can it be concluded that her students are studying less than the average of all students at the university?

<u>Step 1</u>: State the hypotheses and identify the claim.

Since the claim is about the average number of hours studied per week, the parameter is μ and the claim is that $\mu < 5$. The claim is about the inequality or "less than" then the claim is H_1. Since H_1 is the alternative hypothesis, the negation is $\mu \geq 5$ but for the null hypothesis we only use "equals" thus, H_0 is $\mu = 5$

H_0: $\mu = 5$

H_1: $\mu < 5$ (claim)

Since H_1 is "less than," this is a left-tailed test.

<u>Step 2</u>: Find the critical value.

<u>We are given the population standard deviation</u> σ so we use the z test. Note: $\sigma = 90$ minutes which is 1.5 hours, so $\sigma = 1.5$. Since $\alpha = 0.05$, we can use the t table to find the critical z value.

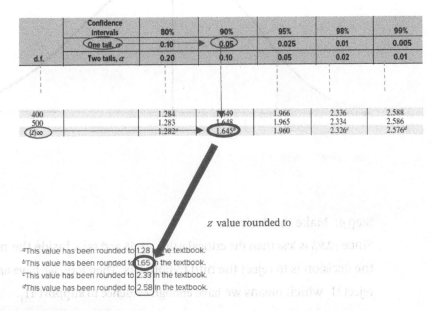

Confidence Intervals	80%	90%	95%	98%	99%
One tail, α	0.10	0.05	0.025	0.01	0.005
d.f. Two tails, α	0.20	0.10	0.05	0.02	0.01
400	1.284	1.649	1.966	2.336	2.588
500	1.283	1.648	1.965	2.334	2.586
$(z)\infty$	1.282[a]	1.645[b]	1.960	2.326[c]	2.576[d]

z value rounded to

[a]This value has been rounded to 1.28 in the textbook.
[b]This value has been rounded to 1.65 in the textbook.
[c]This value has been rounded to 2.33 in the textbook.
[d]This value has been rounded to 2.58 in the textbook.

Since this is a left-tailed test, the critical z value will be negative, so $z = -1.65$

<u>Step 3</u>: Compute the test value.

It is helpful to then plot the test value against the critical value on the same set of axes.

From the problem, we had the hypothesized mean $\mu = 5$. The sample size was 20 so $n = 20$ and the mean of that sample was 3, so $\bar{x} = 4$.

$$z = \frac{\bar{x} - \mu}{\sigma / \sqrt{n}} = \frac{4 - 5}{1.5 / \sqrt{20}} \approx -2.98$$

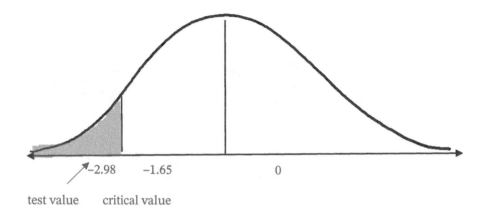

−2.98   −1.65   0

test value   critical value

Step 4: Make the decision.

Since −2.98 is less than the critical value −1.65 and falls inside the rejection region, the decision is to reject the null hypothesis. Therefore, we have enough evidence to reject H_o which means we have enough evidence to support H_1.

Step 5: Summarize the results.

Since the claim was H_1, there is enough evidence to support the claim that the average hours spent studying for her class is less than 4 hours per week.

b. At the time of graduation, college students have accumulated debts from their student loans. The average student loan debt at the time of graduation is $40,000. Some colleges claim that the average student loan debt at the time of graduation is not equal to $40,000. A random sample of 15 students is collected and their average debt at the time of graduation was $43,500 with a standard deviation of $8000. At the 0.05 significance level, is there enough evidence to support the colleges' claim?

Step 1: State the hypotheses and identify the claim.

214

Since the claim is about the average amount in dollars, the parameter is μ and the claim is that $\mu \neq 40000$. The claim is about the inequality or "not equal to" then the claim is H_1. Since H_1 is the alternative hypothesis, the negation is $\mu = 40000$ so H_0 is $\mu = 40000$

H_0: $\mu = 40000$

H_1: $\mu \neq 40000$ (claim)

Since H_1 is "not equal to," this is a two-tailed test.

Step 2: Find the critical value.

Since σ is unknown, s is given and $n \leq 30$, we use the t test.

Since we have $n = 15$, the degrees of freedom d.f. $= n - 1 = 15 - 1 = 14$. We use the t table. Refer to the row where d.f. $= 14$ at $\propto = 0.05$ two tails under obtain a t critical value of 2.145.

d.f.	Confidence Intervals	80%	90%	95%	98%	99%
	One tail, α	0.10	0.05	0.025	0.01	0.005
	Two tails, α	0.20	0.10	0.05	0.02	0.01
1		3.078	6.314	12.706	31.821	63.657
2		1.886	2.920	4.303	6.965	9.925
3		1.638	2.353	3.182	4.541	5.841
4		1.533	2.132	2.776	3.747	4.604
5		1.476	2.015	2.571	3.365	4.032
6		1.440	1.943	2.447	3.143	3.707
7		1.415	1.895	2.365	2.998	3.499
8		1.397	1.860	2.306	2.896	3.355
9		1.383	1.833	2.262	2.821	3.250
10		1.372	1.812	2.228	2.764	3.169
11		1.363	1.796	2.201	2.718	3.106
12		1.356	1.782	2.179	2.681	3.055
13		1.350	1.771	2.160	2.650	3.012
14		1.345	1.761	2.145	2.624	2.977
15		1.341	1.753	2.131	2.602	2.947

Since the test is two tailed, the critical values are $t = \pm 2.145$.

Step 3: Compute the test value using the formula.

215

It is helpful to then plot the test value against the critical value(s) on the same set of axes.

From the problem, we had the hypothesized mean $\mu = 40000$. The sample size was 15 so $n = 15$, and the mean of that sample was 43,500, so $\bar{x} = 43500$. The standard deviation of the sample was 8000 so $s = 8000$

$$t = \frac{\bar{x} - \mu}{s / \sqrt{n}} = \frac{43500 - 40000}{8000 / \sqrt{15}} \approx 1.69$$

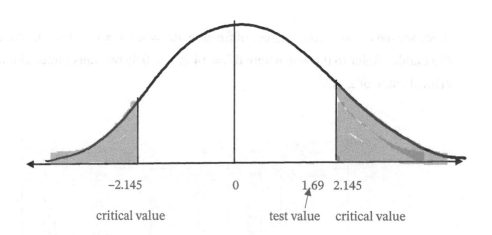

−2.145		0	1.69	2.145
critical value			test value	critical value

Step 4: Make the decision.

Since the test value, 1.69, falls between the two critical values (falls in the noncritical region), the decision is to not reject the null hypothesis. Therefore, we do not have enough evidence to reject H_o , which means we do not have enough evidence to support H_1.

Step 5: Summarize the results.

216

Since the claim was H_1, we do not have enough evidence to support the claim that the average student loan debt at the time of graduation is not equal to $40,000.

In the previous examples, we used the traditional approach whereby the test value is compared to the critical value. The critical value is the cutoff for the rejection region (also known as the critical region). The other approach called the *P*-value method compares the tail area that is cutoff by the test value to the level of significance α.

Reject H_0 when *P*-value $\leq \alpha$

Do not reject H_0 when *P*-value $> \alpha$

Since the *P*-value is the tail area at the cutoff test value, for two-tailed tests the *P*-value is the total of both tails. By symmetry, the *P*-value for a two-tailed test is twice the tail area for the cutoff at one of the test values.

Outline for the *P*-value Hypothesis Testing

1. State the hypotheses (null and alternative) and identify the claim.
2. Compute the test value (using the formula).
3. Find the *P*-value.
4. Make the decision to reject or not reject the null hypothesis.
5. Summarize the results about the claim.

Example:

Return to the previous examples. Use the *P*-value method of hypothesis testing.

c. At a university, a professor is concerned that students are spending too little time studying for her class. The average number of hours per week that all university students study for each class is 5 hours. In a random sample of 20 students, the average number of hours per week that students studying for her class was 4 hours. The population standard deviation was 90 minutes. At the 0.05 level of significance, can it be concluded that her students are studying are less than the average of all students at the university?

Step 1: State the hypotheses (null and alternative) and identify the claim.

Since the claim is about the average number of hours studied per week, the parameter is μ and the claim is that and the claim is that $\mu < 5$. The claim is about the inequality or "less than" then the claim is H_1. Since H_1 is the alternative hypothesis, the negation is $\mu \geq 5$ but for the null hypothesis we only use "equals" thus, H_0 is $\mu = 5$

H_0: $\mu = 5$

H_1: $\mu < 5$ (claim)

Since H_1 is "less than," this is a left-tailed test.

Step 2: Compute the test value using the formula.

It is helpful to then plot the test value against the critical value on the same set of axes.

From the problem, we had the hypothesized mean $\mu = 5$. The sample size was 20 so $n = 20$ and the mean of that sample was 3, so $\overline{x} = 4$.

$$z = \frac{\overline{x} - \mu}{\sigma / \sqrt{n}} = \frac{4 - 5}{1.5 / \sqrt{20}} \approx -2.98$$

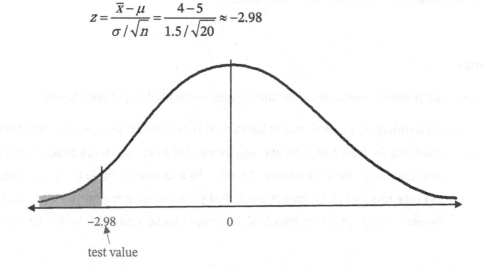

Step 3: Find the *p*-value.

Since this is a left-tailed test, the *P*-value is the area to the left of $z = -2.98$. To find the area to the left of $z = -2.98$, we refer to the z table and look for the area or probability for -2.98.

z	.00	.01	.02	.03	.04	.05	.06	.07	.08	.09
−3.4	.0003	.0003	.0003	.0003	.0003	.0003	.0003	.0003	.0003	.0002
−3.3	.0005	.0005	.0005	.0004	.0004	.0004	.0004	.0004	.0004	.0003
−3.2	.0007	.0007	.0006	.0006	.0006	.0006	.0006	.0005	.0005	.0005
−3.1	.0010	.0009	.0009	.0009	.0008	.0008	.0008	.0008	.0007	.0007
−3.0	.0013	.0013	.0013	.0012	.0012	.0011	.0011	.0011	.0010	.0010
−2.9	.0019	.0018	.0018	.0017	.0016	.0016	.0015	.0015	.0014	.0014
−2.8	.0026	.0025	.0024	.0023	.0023	.0022	.0021	.0021	.0020	.0019
−2.7	.0035	.0034	.0033	.0032	.0031	.0030	.0029	.0028	.0027	.0026

The area to the left of $z = -2.98$ is 0.0014. Therefore, the *P*-value is 0.0014.

Step 4: Make the decision to reject or not reject the null hypothesis.
Since $0.0014 < 0.05$ then the *P*-value $\leq \propto$, as such we have enough evidence to reject H_o and enough evidence to support H_1. The decision is to reject the null hypothesis.

Step 5: Summarize the results about the claim.
Since the claim was H_1, we have enough evidence to support the claim that the average hours spent studying for her class is less than 4 hours per week.

d. At the time of graduation, college students have accumulated debts from their student loans. The average student loan debt at the time of graduation is $40,000. Some colleges claim that the average student loan debt at the time of graduation is not equal to $40,000. A random sample of 15 students is collected and their average debt at the time of graduation was $43,500 with a standard deviation of

$8000. At the 0.05 significance level, is there enough evidence to support the colleges' claim?

Step 1: State the hypotheses (null and alternative) and identify the claim.

Since the claim is about the average amount in dollars, the parameter is μ and the claim is that $\mu \neq 40000$. The claim is about the inequality or "not equal to" then the claim is H_1. Since H_1 is the alternative hypothesis, the negation is $\mu = 40000$ so H_0 is $\mu = 40000$

H_0: $\mu = 40000$

H_1: $\mu \neq 40000$ (claim)

Since H_1 is "not equal to," this is a two-tailed test.

Step 2: Compute the test value using the formula.

Since σ is unknown, s is given and $n \leq 30$, we use the t test. Compute the test value using the formula.

From the problem, we had the hypothesized mean $\mu = 40000$. The sample size was 15 so $n = 15$ and the mean of that sample was 43,500, so $\bar{x} = 43500$. The standard deviation of the sample was 8000 so $s = 8000$

$$t = \frac{\bar{x} - \mu}{s / \sqrt{n}} = \frac{43500 - 40000}{8000 / \sqrt{15}} \approx 1.69$$

Step 3: Find the P-value.

Since this is a two-tailed test, the P-value is twice the area to the right of $t = 1.69$. To find the area to the right of $t = 1.69$, we refer to the t table and look for the approximate area or probability for a one tail 1.69. Since we have $n = 15$, the degrees of freedom d.f. $= n - 1 = 15 - 1 = 14$. We use the t table. Refer to the row

220

where d.f. = 14 and observe that 1.69 falls between the *t* values 1.345 and 1.771. This means that the area for one tail falls between $\alpha = 0.10$ and $\alpha = 0.05$ whereas the area for the two tails falls between $\alpha = 0.20$ and $\alpha = 0.10$. Since this is a two-tailed test, the *P*-value falls between 0.20 and 0.10.

P-value for the two tails falls between $\alpha = 0.20$ and 0.10

d.f.	Confidence Intervals	80%	90%	95%	98%	99%
	One tail, α	0.10	0.05	0.025	0.01	0.005
	Two tails, α	0.20	0.10	0.05	0.02	0.01
1		3.078	6.314	12.706	31.821	63.657
2		1.886	2.920	4.303	6.965	9.925
3		1.638	2.353	3.182	4.541	5.841
4		1.533	2.132	2.776	3.747	4.604
5		1.476	2.015	2.571	3.365	4.032
6		1.440	1.943	2.447	3.143	3.707
7		1.415	1.895	2.365	2.998	3.499
8		1.397	1.860	2.306	2.896	3.355
9		1.383	1.833	2.262	2.821	3.250
10		1.372	1.812	2.228	2.764	3.169
11		1.363	1.796	2.201	2.718	3.106
12		1.356	1.782	2.179	2.681	3.055
13		1.350	1.771	2.160	2.650	3.012
14		1.345	1.761	2.145	2.624	2.977
15		1.341	1.753	2.131	2.602	2.947

t value = 1.69 falls

$$0.10 < P\text{-value} < 0.20$$

We do not have the exact *P*-value, but we do know that is it greater than $\alpha = 0.10$.

Step 4: Make the decision to reject or not reject the null hypothesis.
Since the *P*-value > $\alpha = 0.10$, we do not have enough evidence to reject H_o. Thus, we do not have enough evidence to support H_1.
Step 5: Summarize the results about the claim.
Since the claim was H_1, we do not have enough evidence to support the claim that the average student loan debt at the time of graduation is not equal to $40,000.

Your Turn to Practice

Perform hypotheses tests on each of the following situations using both methods:

    i.   Use the traditional method of hypothesis testing.

ii.   Use the *P*-value method.

1. With cell phone service costs dropping, a new 2017 ad from a cell phone carrier states that their average monthly bill for cell phone service including taxes for two smartphones is $100.   Another carrier advertises more options including additional employer discounts to further lower the monthly bill as well as more expensive plans for those seeking more services. As such the other carrier claims that the average monthly bill is not $100.   A random sample of 30 customers results in an average monthly bill of $115. The population standard deviation is $45.   At the 0.05 level of significance, is the other carrier's claim correct that the average monthly bill is not $100?

2. The average lifespan of a particular car battery is 4 years. Car drivers believe that the average lifespan of their car batteries is lower than that. A random sample of 20 cars is collected and the mean battery life was 3 years with a standard deviation of 1.2 years.   Can it be concluded that the average car better life span is lower than 4 years? Use a 0.01 level of significance.

3. Drivers traveling north and south at a busy intersection get frustrated with the signal light at that corner. According to the local county transportation agency, the average wait time at that red light for those traveling north and south is only 2.5 minutes. The population standard deviation is assumed to be 0.75 minutes. The drivers traveling north and south believe that in fact the wait time is much higher than that. A study is conducted and a random sample of 10 drivers' wait time at that signal light traveling north and south is 3 minutes. At a level of significance of 0.10, is the complaint from the car drivers correct?

Chapter 9 Graphing Lines

9.1 Plot Ordered Pairs

In algebra when graphing one-dimensional graphs, we use a number line typically in a horizontal fashion. As we saw in Section 1.1, the number line represents the real number system and is infinite in both directions.

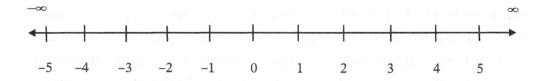

In a two-dimensional case, we graph a horizontal number line and intersect it with a vertical number line. We call the horizontal number line the x-axis, and the vertical number line the y-axis. The point of intersection is at the zero value of each line represented by the ordered pair $(0, 0)$ also known as the origin. Since the graph is two dimensional, the points are given as ordered pairs (x, y). The x coordinate moves in the horizontal direction, while the y coordinate moves in the vertical direction.

The intersection of these two lines forms four regions known as quadrants. We number the four quadrants in a counter-clockwise manner starting with Quadrant I at the top right. See below.

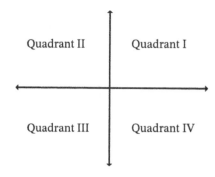

When plotting points on this graph, we start at the origin (0, 0) and first move horizontally (left or right) depending on the sign of the x-coordinate and then move vertically (up or down) depending on the sign of the y-coordinate. We can summarize the characteristics of the four quadrants as follows:

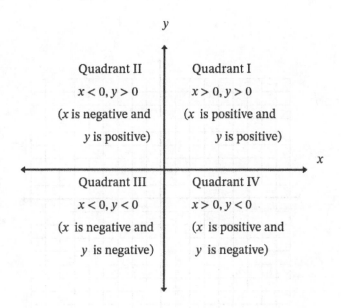

Example: Identify the ordered for each point plotted on the graph.

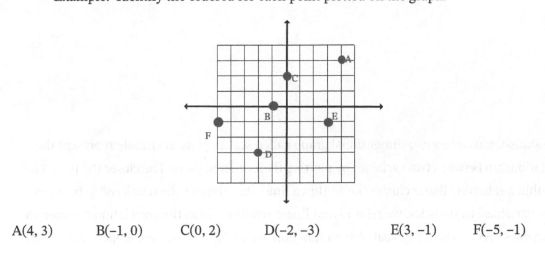

A(4, 3)   B(−1, 0)   C(0, 2)   D(−2, −3)   E(3, −1)   F(−5, −1)

225

Your Turn to Practice

Plot the following plots on the graph below. Label the points with their respective letters.

   a. (0, 0)   b. (9, 5)   c.(−3, 2)   d. (0, 1)   e. (4, −6)   f. (−7, −2) g. (−8, 0)

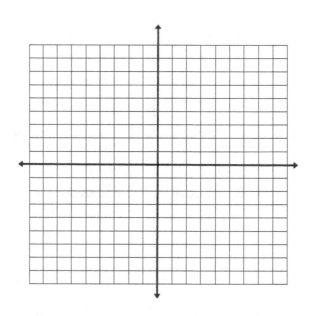

In statistics, we use a two-dimensional graph called scatter plots to visually represent the relationship between two variables by plotting their ordered pairs. The closer the points lie within a relatively linear cluster (i.e. within a line), the stronger the relationship between the variables. In statistics, we refer to that linear relationship as the correlation between the variables. As we do in a typical algebra function, we assign x to be the independent variable

226

and y to be the dependent variable if we find that there is a relationship between the two variables. When such a relationship exists, we say that output y value depends on the input x value.

In certain applications is statistics when both variables cannot take on negative values, the graph of the scatter plot is only in the first quadrant.

Below are four examples of scatter plots. Scatter plots #1 and #2 show a linear relationship between x and y.

Scatter plot #3 has the all points scattered indicating that there is no linear relationship between the variables.

Scatter plot #4 shows that regardless of the value of the variable x, the variable y remains constant.

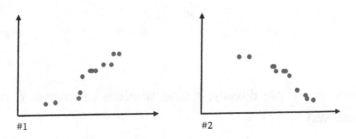

#1   #2

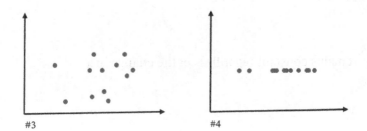

#3   #4

227

9.2 Slope-Intercept Form of a Line

Given two points, the slope of a line is defined as the difference between the y coordinates of those points divided by the difference between the x coordinates of those points. Let m represent the slope between two points $\left(x_1, y_1\right)$ and $\left(x_2, y_2\right)$ then

$$m = \frac{y_2 - y_1}{x_2 - x_1}$$

There are four possibilities for the slope m: positive slope ($m > 0$), negative slope ($m < 0$), zero slope ($m = 0$), and an undefined slope (m is undefined). For Statistics, we only apply the first three cases.

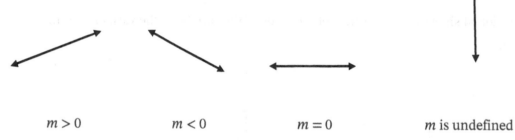

| $m > 0$ | $m < 0$ | $m = 0$ | m is undefined |

When $m > 0$, both x and y vary directly, in other words as x increases, y increases (or as x decreases, y decreases).

When $m < 0$, x and y vary inversely, in other words as x increases, y decreases (or as x decreases, y increases).

When $m = 0$, y remains constant regardless of the change in x.

Examples:

Compute the slope of the line passing through the given points and comment on whether the slope is positive, negative, zero, or undefined.

a. (7, 2) (9, 10)

$$m = \frac{10-2}{9-7} = \frac{8}{2} = 4$$

This is a positive slope.

b. (3, –1) (–4, 8)

$$m = \frac{8-(-1)}{-4-3} = \frac{9}{-7} = -\frac{9}{7}$$

This is a negative slope.

c. (6, 5) (–6, –5)

$$m = \frac{-5-5}{-6-6} = \frac{-10}{-12} = \frac{5}{6}$$

This is a positive slope.

d. (6, –2) (8, –2)

229

$$m = \frac{(-2)-(-2)}{8-6} = \frac{0}{2} = 0$$

Here the slope is zero, meaning that the line is horizontal.

e. $(-3, 7)$ $(-3, 6)$

$$m = \frac{6-7}{-3-(-3)} = \frac{-1}{0}$$ which is an undefined number.

Therefore, there is no slope.

f. $(-9, 0)$ $(0, -9)$

$$m = \frac{-9-0}{0-(-9)} = \frac{-9}{9} = -1$$

This is a negative slope.

Your Turn to Practice

Compute the slope of the passing through the given points.

1. $(8, 1)$ $(15, 23)$

2. (–11, –9) (7, –9)

3. (3, –1) (–4, 8)

4. (–5, 0) (0, –5)

5. (4, –2) (–4, –9)

6. (–8, 4) (–8, 3)

7. (–14, 18) (14, –10)

We can use the value of the slope and the y coordinate at the y-axis, which is called the y-intercept, to write the equation of a line. Using m for the slope and b for the y-intercept, we write the general equation of a line in the form: $y = mx + b$. This is called slope-intercept form.

[NOTE: In statistics, we rewrite the formula as $y = a + bx$, such that a is the y-intercept and b is the slope.]

For the remainder of this section, we will use continue to use the algebraic form.

Examples:

Write the equation of the line in slope-intercept form $y = mx + b$ using the given information.

    a. Write the equation of the line with a slope of $-\dfrac{5}{4}$ and a y-intercept of 7.

        Substituting $m = -\dfrac{5}{4}$ and $b = 7$, the equation of the line is $y = -\dfrac{5}{4}x + 7$.

    b. Write the equation of the line with a slope of 9 and a y-intercept of 0.

        Substituting $m = 9$ and $b = 0$, the equation of the line is $y = 9x + 0$.

$$\text{or } y = 9x$$

    c. Write the equation of the line with a slope of 0 and a y-intercept of –2.

        Substituting $m = 0$ and $b = -2$, the equation of the line is $y = 0x - 2$.

$$\text{or } y = -2$$

    d. Write the equation of the line with a slope of $\dfrac{2}{3}$ passing through the point (6, –4).

        Substituting $m = \dfrac{2}{3}$ and b is unknown, the equation of the line is $y = \dfrac{2}{3}x + b$.

        We need to substitute the given ordered pair in for x and y to solve for b. Given the point (6, –4), we substitute $x = 6$ and $y = -4$.

$$-4 = \frac{2}{3}(6) + b$$

$$-4 = 4 + b$$

$$-8 = b$$

Substituting $m = \frac{2}{3}$ and $b = -8$, the equation of the line is $y = \frac{2}{3}x - 8$

e. Write the equation of the line passing through the points (5, 8) and (–3, 7).

In this case, both m and b are unknown, so first we must compute the slope value m and then solve for b.

$$m = \frac{y_2 - y_1}{x_2 - x_1} = \frac{7 - 8}{-3 - 5} = \frac{-1}{-8} = \frac{1}{8}$$

Substituting $m = \frac{1}{8}$ and b is unknown, the equation of the line is $y = \frac{1}{8}x + b$.

We need to substitute one of the given ordered pairs in for x and y to solve for b. *[NOTE: Either point may be selected.]* Using the point (5, 8), we substitute $x = 5$ and $y = 8$.

$$8 = \frac{1}{8}(5) + b$$

$$8 = \frac{5}{8} + b$$

$$\frac{59}{8} = b$$

Substituting $m = \frac{1}{8}$ and $b = \frac{59}{8}$, the equation of the line is $y = \frac{1}{8}x + \frac{59}{8}$.

Your Turn to Practice

Write the equation of the line in slope-intercept form $y = mx + b$ using the given information.

1. The slope of $\dfrac{8}{11}$ and a y-intercept of 3.

2. The slope of 0 and a y-intercept of 6.

3. The slope of $\dfrac{9}{17}$ and a y-intercept of $\dfrac{1}{13}$.

4. The slope of $-\dfrac{6}{5}$ and a y-intercept of 0.

5. The slope of $-\dfrac{1}{2}$ passing through the point (0, 3).

234

6. The slope of $\frac{5}{7}$ passing through the point (35, 10).

7. The line passing through the points (0, 6) and (3, 0).

8. The line passing through the points (2, –4) and (–5, –8).

We can use the slope-intercept form of a line to graph quickly a line. Since the slope is the difference between the y coordinates of those points divided by the difference between the x coordinates of those points or sometimes simply stated as the rise (change in y) over the run (change in x), we can plot one point and move to the next point using the slope. Given the equation in slope intercept form, we use the y-intercept point (0, b) as the initial point and then move to the next point using the slope value.

235

Examples:

Graph the given line using the given information.

a. $y = \dfrac{7}{5}x - 7$

Plot $(0, -7)$ since the y-intercept which is $b = -7$.

Use $m = \dfrac{7}{5}$ and move 7 units up and 5 to the right.

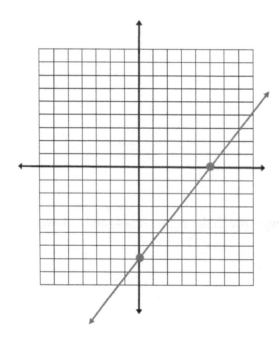

b. $y = -\dfrac{3}{2}x + 6$

Plot (0, 6) since the y-intercept which is $b = 6$. Since the slope is negative, either the vertical or the horizontal movement will be in the negative direction but not both negative at the same time. *NOTE: If both are negative then the slope would be positive.*

Either use $m = -\dfrac{3}{2} = \dfrac{-3}{2}$ and move 3 units down and 2 to the right

OR use $m = -\dfrac{3}{2} = \dfrac{3}{-2}$ and move 3 units up and 2 to the left.

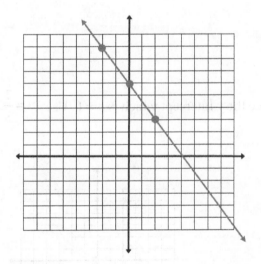

c. $y = -x + 2$

Plot (0, 2) since the y-intercept which is $b = 2$.

Either use $m = -1 = -\dfrac{1}{1} = \dfrac{-1}{1}$ and move 1 unit down and 1 to the right

237

OR use $m = -1 = -\dfrac{1}{1} = \dfrac{1}{-1}$ and move 1 unit up and 1 to the left.

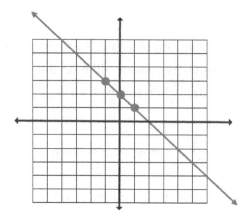

d. $y = \dfrac{2}{3}x$

Plot (0, 0) since the y-intercept which is $b = 0$. Use $m = \dfrac{2}{3}$ and move 2 units up and 3 to the right.

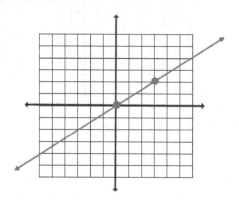

238

e. $y = 4$

Plot $(0, 4)$ since the y-intercept which is $b = 4$.

Use $m = 0$ Do not move up or down. Only move horizontally.

With a zero slope, the line is a horizontal line passing through the y-intercept point.

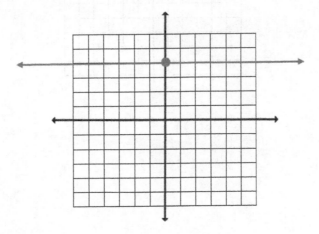

Your Turn to Practice

Graph the given line using the given information.

1. $y = -\dfrac{5}{4}x + 5$

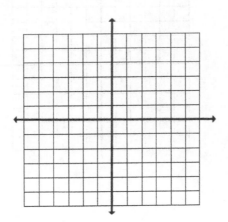

2. $y = -3$

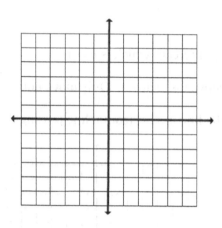

3. $y = -\dfrac{3}{5}x$

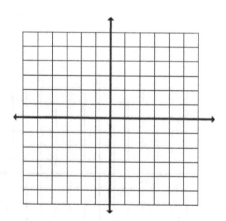

4. $y = -\dfrac{1}{3}x - 2$

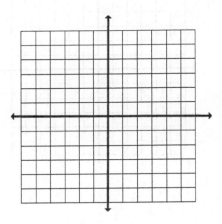

5. $y = \dfrac{3}{2}x + 1$

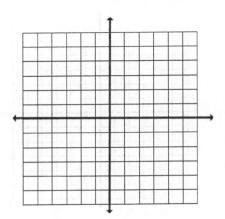

6. $y = -x - 4$

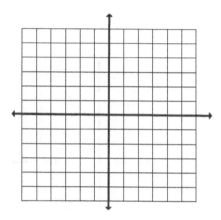

7. $y = 2x - 6$

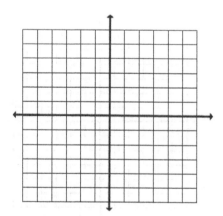

Answers for Your Turn to Practice Exercises

Chapter 1

<u>1.1</u>

1. Rational. Also: Natural, Whole and Integer.

2. Rational. Also: Integer.

3. Rational. We can also reduce this to 9. This is also: Natural, Whole and Integer.

4. Irrational.

5. This is a terminating decimal. Rational only.

6. This is a repeating decimal. Rational only.

7. Rational only.

8. Irrational.

9. This decimal does not repeat and does terminate. Irrational.

10. Rational. Also: Whole and Integer.

11. Rational. We can also reduce this to 7. This is also: Natural, Whole and Integer.

<u>1.2</u>

1. <   2. <   3. =   4. >   5. >

<u>1.3</u>

1. 10   2. 65   3. 59   4. 9   5. $\sqrt{3.7} \approx 1.92$ 6. $\dfrac{11}{14}$

<u>1.4</u>

1. 35.55 – 35.65

2. 0.00023485 – 0.00023495

3. 2.74805 – 2.74815

4. 56.5 – 57.5

5. 1.975 – 1.985

6. 13.245 – 13.255

1.5

1. Ratio, since there are differences between heights, and there is an absolute zero.

2. Ordinal since the classifications have meaning based on their ranking.

3. Nominal since the classifications are names.

4. Interval, since there are differences between temperature readings, but there is no absolute zero.

5. Nominal since the classifications are names.

Chapter 2

2.1

First set

1. 4 is in the ones places; 6 is in the tens place; 8 is in the hundreds place;

    0 is in the thousands place; 2 is in the ten-thousands place

2. 5 is in the hundreds place; 7 is in the tens place; 9 is in the ones places;

    4 is in the tenths place; 8 is in the hundredths place; 6 is in the thousandths place;

    3 is in the ten-thousandths place; 1 is in the hundred-thousandths place

Second set

1. 29.5

2. 29.500

3. 32,594.051

4. 32,594.05

5. 98

6. 97.8

7. 0.00

8. 0.00087

9. 0.000865

10. 0.000000215

2.2

1. 530%

2. 2.9%

3. 44%

4. 75%

6. 58% *Two significant digits; 57.7% Three significant digits); 57.73% Four significant digits.*

7. 0.0094%

8. 67% *Two significant digits; 66.7% Three significant digits); 66.67% Four significant digits.*

9. 0.01987

10. 0.64

11. 1

12. 0.005

13. 0.0000354

14. 2.6

15. 0.99

2.3

The number of minutes spent on one phone call	Cumulative Number of people (Cumulative Frequency)
-0.5 – 5.5	8
5.5 – 10.5	48
10.5 – 15.5	64
15.5 – 20.5	70
20.5 – 25.5	74
25.5 – 30.5	77
30.5 – 35.5	79
Above 35.5	80

2.4

The number of minutes spent on one phone call	Relative Frequency
-0.5 – 5.5	0.1
5.5 – 10.5	0.5
10.5 – 15.5	0.2
15.5 – 20.5	0.075
20.5 – 25.5	0.05
25.5 – 30.5	0.0375
30.5 – 35.5	0.025
Above 35.5	0.0125

The number of minutes spent on one phone call	% of people
-0.5 – 5.5	10%
5.5 – 10.5	50%
10.5 – 15.5	20%
15.5 – 20.5	7.5%
20.5 – 25.5	5%
25.5 – 30.5	3.75%
30.5 – 35.5	2.5%
Above 35.5	1.25%

The number of minutes spent on one phone call	Cumulative Relative Frequency
-0.5 – 5.5	0.1
5.5 – 10.5	0.6
10.5 – 15.5	0.8
15.5 – 20.5	0.875
20.5 – 25.5	0.925
25.5 – 30.5	0.9625
30.5 – 35.5	0.9875
Above 35.5	1

The number of minutes spent on one phone call	Cumulative % of people
-0.5 – 5.5	10%
5.5 – 10.5	30%
10.5 – 15.5	80%
15.5 – 20.5	87.5%
20.5 – 25.5	92.5%
25.5 – 30.5	96.25%
30.5 – 35.5	98.75%
Above 35.5	100%

2.5

The number of minutes shopping on-line (Class Midpoints)	Number of people (Frequency)
5.2	10
15.7	19
26.2	11
36.7	8
47.2	9
57.7	1
68.2	2

The number of minutes shopping on-line (Class Boundaries)	Number of people (Frequency)
-0.05 – 10.45	10
10.45 – 20.95	19
20.95 – 31.45	11
31.45 – 41.95	8
41.95 – 52.45	9
52.45 – 62.95	1
62.95 – 73.45	2

2.6

1. *Answers may vary.* <u>One conclusion</u>: The most popular ice cream flavor is vanilla.

2. *Answers may vary.* <u>One conclusion</u>: Most people spent somewhere between 10.5 to 20.9 minutes shopping online. Using the class midpoint, we could also say that the most time spent shopping online was approximately 15.7 minutes.

3. *Answers may vary.* <u>One conclusion</u>: Thursday is the day with the highest TV viewing.

   The bars on the Pareto chart which represent the frequencies appear in descending order.

4. *Answers may vary.* <u>One conclusion</u>: The most popular weekly summer camp activity is baseball.

Chapter 3

3.1

1. The population variance for the height of young adult males is 36 inches squared.

2. The population standard deviation travel time to work in the morning is 16 minutes.

3. The population average lifespan of factory paint for automobiles is 10 years.

3.2

1. a. $X_1 = 1.3$ b. $X_2 = 5.2$ c. $X_5 = 44.7$ d. $X_8 = 61.2$ e. $X_{10} = 61.8$ f. $X_{12} = 77.5$

2. a. $X_1 = 59.97$ b. $X_2 = 77.10$ c. $X_3 = 79.26$ d. $X_4 = 81.05$ e. $X_5 = 94.56$

   f. $X_6 = 99.22$ g. $X_7 = 100.26$

3.3

1. 34.6   2. 71.5   3. 25.85 minutes

3.4

1. $n = \pm 10$

2. $x = -4, 14$

3. $y = \pm 5\sqrt{2} \approx \pm 7.1$

4. $\sigma = 4$ (only positive since standard deviation is never negative)

5. $s = 3$ (only positive since standard deviation is never negative)

6. $s = 2\sqrt{21} \approx 9.2$ (only positive since standard deviation is never negative)

3.5

Approximately 68% of adults sleep 350 to 370 minutes.

Approximately 95% of adults sleep 340 to 380 minutes.

Approximately 99.7% of adults sleep 330 to 390 minutes.

3.6

1. Minimum = 25 $Q_1 = 100$ Median = 125 $Q_3 = 175$ Maximum = 200

2. Minimum = 0 $Q_1 = 100$ Median = 200 $Q_3 = 300$ Maximum = 900

3. Minimum = 50 $Q_1 = 100$ Median = 125 $Q_3 = 150$ Maximum = 200

Chapter 4

4.1

First Set

1. {a, b, c, d, h}

2. {Monday, Tuesday, Wednesday, Thursday, Friday}

3. {3, 4, 5, 6}

4. {(H,H), (H,T), (T,H), (T,T)}

5. {(H,H,H), (H,H,T), (H,T,H), (H,T,T), (T,H,H), (T,H,T), (T,T,H), (T,T,T)}

6. {(0,0), (0, 1), (0, 2), (0, 3),

   (1,0), (1, 1), (1, 2), (1, 3)

   (2,0), (2, 1), (2, 2), (2, 3)

   (3,0), (3, 1), (3, 2), (3, 3)}

Second Set

1. NO 2. NO 3. YES 4. NO

4.2

1. 65%   2. 1.1%   3. 0.274   4. 0.9999988   5. $P(R) = \dfrac{3}{8}; P(\bar{R}) = \dfrac{5}{8}$ 6. $\dfrac{337}{365}$

4.3

1. Low chance

2. The same chance to occur or not occur

3. Will always occur

4. High chance

5. Will never occur

4.4

First Set

1. a. 0.077 b. 0.0767   2. a. 0.17 b. 0.167   3. a. 1.0 b 1.00

Second Set

1. 5.87×10^3 2. 5.00×10^{-4} 3. 7.67×10^1 4. 8.42×10^{-2} 5. 1.43×10^5

6. 3.75×10^{-2} 7. 7×10^{-2} 8. 4.67×10^{-8}

Third Set

1. 4,590   2. 0.0874   3. 0.00000128   4. 65,200   5. 0.0959

Fourth Set

1. 7.67×10^{-2} 2. 1.00×10^0 3. 1.67×10^{-1}

4.5

First Set

1. $\frac{10}{10}$ or 10 to 10   or 10:10 (can be reduced to $\frac{1}{1}$ or 1 to 1 or 1:1)

2. $\frac{4}{9}$ or 4 to 9 or 4:9

3. $\frac{17}{3}$ or 17 to 3 or 17:3

Second Set

1. Odds for A 23:40; Odds against A 40:23

2. Odds for B 8:9; Odds against B 9:8

3. Odds for C 2:4 (or 1:2); Odds against C 4:2 (or 2:1)

4. Odds for D 3:3 (or 1:1); Odds against D 3:3 (or 1:1)

<u>4.6</u>

First Set

1. $x = 3$ 2. $x = 0.16$ 3. $x = \frac{7}{2}$ 4. $x = \frac{6}{7}$

Second Set

1. $P(C|D) = 0.036$ and $P(D|C) = 0.06$

2. $P(F|E) = 0.12$

3. $P(A|B) = 0.09$

<u>4.7</u>

First Set

1. 720   2. 120   3. 120   4. 6,227,020,800   5. $\frac{1}{8010}$ 6. 2.43×10^{18}

7. $\frac{1}{n+1}$ 8. 40,320

Second Set

1. 20,358,520   2. 70   3. 840

Chapter 5

<u>5.1</u>

1. No, this is not a probability distribution since $\sum P(X) = 0.10 < 1$

As with part (c), each of the individual probabilities is between 0 and 1, but the sum is less than 1. Again, BOTH must hold for a probability distribution to be valid.

2. Yes, this is a valid probability distribution since the two conditions are satisfied.

      i) $\sum P(X) = 0.41 + 0.10 + 0.29 + 0.20 = 1$

      ii)   Each $P(X)$ is between 0 and 1.

3. No, this is not a probability distribution since $\sum P(X) = \dfrac{3}{2} \neq 1$.

In this case, each of the individual probabilities is between 0 and 1, but the sum is greater than 1. Again, BOTH must hold for a probability distribution to be valid.

4. No, this is not a probability distribution since $\sum P(X) = \dfrac{36}{25} \neq 1$.

In this case, each of the individual probabilities is between 0 and 1, but the sum is greater than 1. Again, BOTH must hold for a probability distribution to be valid.

5. No, this is not a valid probability distribution. $P(15)$ is negative which is impossible since $P(X)$ must be between 0 and 1.

5.2

1. $0   2. –$1.40   3. –$1.36

5.3

First Set

1. No. Condition #4 is not satisfied since $p = \dfrac{1}{5} = 0.2$ for the first 60 questions and

$p = \dfrac{1}{4} = 0.25$ for the last 20 questions.

2. No. Condition #1 is not satisfied since the outcome of each question is not only success or failure since partial credit is awarded.

3. Yes. All 4 conditions are satisfied.

4. No. Condition #1 is not satisfied since the outcome of each question is not only success or failure since partial credit is awarded.

Second Set

1. 0.117 [If using the formula $P(7) = \dfrac{10!}{(10-7)!7!}(0.5)^7(0.5)^{10-7}$ or $_{10}C_7(0.5)^7(0.5)^{10-7}$]

2. 0.001

3. 0.172

4. 0.001

5. 0.945

6. 0.012

7. Table approximately 0.000   Formula: $P(20) = \dfrac{20!}{(20-20)!20!}(0.2)^{20}(0.8)^{20-20} \approx 1.05 \times 10^{-14}$

8. Table approximately 1

Chapter 6

<u>6.1</u>

1.

2.

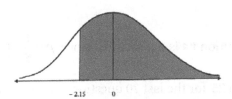

3.

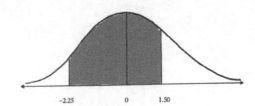

4.

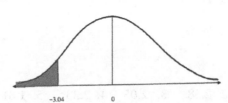

5.

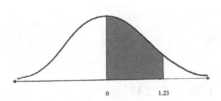

6.

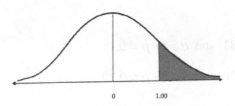

<u>6.2</u>

First Set

1. 0.9772   2. 0.9842   3. 0.3907   4. 0.0012   5. 0.9210   6. 0.1587

Second Set

1. 1.99   2. −1.72   3. −0.59   4. 1.88   5. −2.33   6. ±2.58   7. ±1.04

<u>6.3</u>

1. 0.1335   2. 0.0132   3. 0.9868   4. 0.9992   5. 28.015 ≈ 28   6. 21.22 ≈ 21

7. $X_{MIN} = 18.655 \approx 19$ and $X_{MAX} = 31.345 \approx 31$

<u>6.4</u>

1. 0.2578   2. 0.0045   3. 0.0016   4. 0.0205

Chapter 7

<u>7.1</u>

1. 1.75   2. 2.58   3. 2.05   4. 2.33   5. 1.81   6. 1.88   7. 2.17

<u>7.2</u>

1. $\bar{x} = 15$

2. $\hat{p} = 0.81$ and $\hat{q} = 1 - \hat{p} = 0.19$

3. $\hat{p} = 0.80$ and $\hat{q} = 1 - \hat{p} = 0.20$

4. $\bar{x} = 20$

<u>7.3</u>

First Set

1. 2.500   2. 4.604   3. 1.990   4. 1.699   5. 2.429

Second Set

1. $t_{\alpha/2} = 2.365$ 2. $z_{\alpha/2} = 1.96$ 3. $t_{\alpha/2} = 2.763$ 4. $z_{\alpha/2} = 1.65$

<u>7.4</u>

First Set

1. $12.9 < \mu < 17.1$ Therefore, we are 99% confident that the true mean number of hours weekly spent playing video games is between 12.9 hours and 17.1 hours.

2. $0.818 < p < 0.982$ or $81.8\% < p < 98.2\%$ So, we say with 99% confidence that the true percentage of community college students that plan to transfer to a four-year university upon completion of their Associate in Arts degree is between 81.8% and 98.2%.

3. $0.637 < p < 0.963$ or $63.7\% < p < 96.3\%$ So, we say with 99% confidence that the true percentage of parents who are worried about their kids spending too much time texting is between 63.7% and 96.3%.

4. $19.7 < \mu < 20.3$ Therefore, we are 90% confident that the population mean time spent shopping online at night is between 19.7 minutes and 20.3 minutes.

Second Set

1. Minimum sample size is 12 students.

2. Minimum sample size is 1849 students.

3. Minimum sample size is 1423 students.

Chapter 8

8.1

1. H_0: $\mu = 2$; H_1: $\mu > 2$ (claim); Since H_1 is "greater than," this is a right-tailed test.

2. H_0: $\mu = 2$ (claim); H_1: $\mu \neq 2$; Since H_1 is "not equal to," this is a two-tailed test.

3. H_0: $\sigma = 10$ (claim); H_1: $\sigma > 10$; Since H_1 is "greater than," this is a right-tailed test.

4. H_0: $p = 0.45$ (claim); H_1: $p < 0.45$; Since H_1 is "less than," this is a left-tailed test.

5. H_0: $\mu = 30$; H_1: $\mu < 30$ (claim); Since H_1 is "less than," this is a left-tailed test.

6. H_0: $p = 0.30$ (claim); H_1: $p > 0.30$; Since H_1 is "greater than," this is a right-tailed test.

7. H_0: $\mu_1 = \mu_2$; H_1: $\mu_1 \neq \mu_2$ (claim); Since H_1 is "not equal to," this is a two-tailed test.

8.2

1. <u>Traditional Approach:</u> $H_o: \mu = 100$; $H_1: \mu \neq 100$ (claim); two-tailed test; Critical Values: $z = \pm 1.96$; Test Value: $z = 1.83$; do not reject H_o; We do not have enough evidence to support the claim that the average monthly bill is not $100.

   <u>P-value Approach:</u> $H_o: \mu = 100$; $H_1: \mu \neq 100$ (claim); two-tailed test; Test Value: $z = 1.83$; P-value $= 2(0.336) = 0.0672$; P-value $> \propto$; do not reject H_o; We do not have enough evidence to support the claim that the average monthly bill is not $100.

2. <u>Traditional Approach:</u> $H_o: \mu = 4$; $H_1: \mu < 4$ (claim); left-tailed test; Critical Value: $t = -2.539$; Test Value: $t = -3.73$; reject H_o; We have enough evidence to support the claim that the average car better life span is lower than 4 years.

   <u>P-value Approach:</u> $H_o: \mu = 4$; $H_1: \mu < 4$ (claim); left-tailed test; Test Value: $t = -3.73$; P-value < 0.005; P-value $\leq \propto$; reject H_o; We have enough evidence to support the claim that the average car better life span is lower than 4 years.

3. <u>Traditional Approach:</u> $H_o: \mu = 2.5$; $H_1: \mu > 2.5$ (claim); right-tailed test; Critical Value: $z = 1.28$; Test Value: $z = 2.11$; reject H_o; We have enough evidence to support the claim that the average wait time at that signal light traveling north and south is higher than 2.5 minutes.

   <u>P-value Approach:</u> $H_o: \mu = 2.5$; $H_1: \mu > 2.5$ (claim); right-tailed test; Test Value: $z = 2.11$; P-value $= 0.0174$; P-value $\leq \propto$; reject H_o; We have enough evidence to support the claim that the average wait time at that signal light traveling north and south is higher than 2.5 minutes.

Chapter 9

9.1

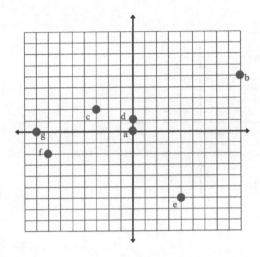

9.2

First Set

1. $\dfrac{22}{7}$ 2. 0   3. $-\dfrac{9}{7}$ 4. -1 5. $\dfrac{7}{8}$ 6. Undefined or no slope   7. -1

Second Set

1. $y = \dfrac{8}{11}x + 3$ 2. $y = 6$ 3. $y = \dfrac{9}{17}x + \dfrac{1}{13}$ 4. $y = -\dfrac{6}{5}x$ 5. $y = -\dfrac{1}{2}x + 3$

6. $y = \dfrac{5}{7}x - 15$ 7. $y = -2x + 6$ 8. $y = \dfrac{4}{7}x - \dfrac{36}{7}$

Third Set

1.

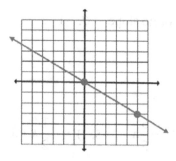

2.

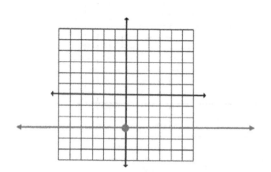

3.

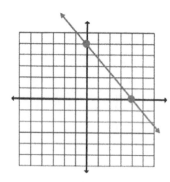

4.

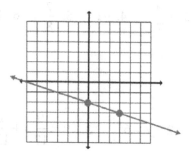

5.

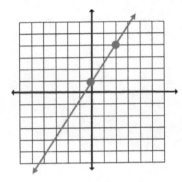

6.

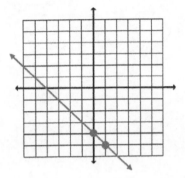

7.

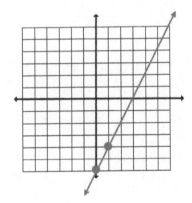